READING 5
FOR YOUNG CATHOLICS

COMPREHENSION

WRITTEN BY
MARY LYNCH

SETON PRESS
FRONT ROYAL, VA

Executive Editor: Dr. Mary Kay Clark
Editors: Seton Staff

Seton Home Study School
1350 Progress Drive
Front Royal, VA 22630
540-636-9990
540-636-1602 fax

For more information, visit us on the Web at www.setonhome.org.
Contact us by e-mail at info@setonhome.org.

ISBN: 978-1-60704-050-7

Cover: Stained-Glass Window from St. Joseph's Catholic Church in Speyer, Germany

Dedicated to the
Sacred Heart of Jesus

Sculpture of Moses in the Church of San Pietro in Vincoli, Rome (Michelangelo).

Contents

This book has been produced through a generous donation from the St. Gerard Foundation. We thank the foundation's board and trustees, and ask the prayers of those who use this book for all who contributed to its completion.

Introduction

To Parents and Students:

This book was written as a help for young students to read for comprehension. With each selection, there is a page of comprehension questions.

Instead of a varied selection of short readings, the readings consist of the story of an Israelite (Jewish) boy, Joe, and his Egyptian friend, Pepi. The story takes place during the time of the plagues and the trip by the Israelite people across the Red Sea, about 1200 years before the birth of Jesus.

Our author, Mary Lynch, did extensive research for this book. Please remember Mrs. Lynch in your prayers, as she was kind enough to volunteer a great deal of her time in writing this book. We hope the pictures and the illustrations help make the story more interesting.

We encourage you to learn more about the people of Israel and the miracles God performed when He freed them with a Mighty Hand from their slavery in Egypt.

Egypt has another important meaning for Catholics. The Holy Family lived there for a few years to escape the persecution of Herod after Our Lord Jesus Christ was born. Also, several saints have lived in Egypt, including the great Saint Anthony of the Desert, the Father of Eastern Monasticism.

Egyptian Background

In ancient Egypt, it was difficult to learn to read and write. It is hard for us to imagine reading or writing without letters that stand for sounds. In some countries, even today, people draw little pictures to represent ideas, rather than letters to represent sounds.

The Egyptians had some alphabet-type letters, but also used many, many picture symbols. In order to be literate, an Egyptian needed to learn hundreds of picture signs representing sounds and ideas. The minimum number of hieroglyphic signs needed was about 200. Researchers found a list of signs used by an Egyptian schoolboy, which consisted of 450 signs! Later, an Egyptian would need to know about 750 signs. If a young ancient Egyptian became a professional scribe, he would need to know about 1,000 signs!

It is not surprising, therefore, that most Egyptians could not read or write. The average Egyptian was a farmer, who grew crops and took care of his animals.

In such an illiterate country, the man who could read and write was considered superior. In fact, he was. He had more knowledge about everything. The professional scribe was a member of the foremost of all professions. The nobles in Egypt were determined to learn to read and write. In fact, the way a lowly boy could rise in society was by learning to read and write. Being a scribe to the king was one of the highest offices in Egypt.

Let's think a little more about this. Do you realize that one out of ten Americans graduating from high school is illiterate? This means they are not learning their alphabet sounds, how to put them together to make words, how to put words together to make sentences, how to put sentences together to make clear thoughts. How can this be? How can this happen?

It is happening for several reasons. First, so many people are looking at pictures, especially television pictures, instead of reading letters, words, sentences, paragraphs, books, magazines, and newspapers.

Second, the process of learning the sounds of letters is called phonics, and even the schools are not teaching phonics very much, or well.

If citizens of a country are illiterate, then they cannot learn more about their work, or about how to do things in the most efficient way, run a store, or run a country. Worst of all, they cannot read one of the most precious gifts given to us by God — His Holy Word, the Bible.

As we thank Jesus for giving us the ability to learn the alphabet, let's also do our best to use our knowledge of the alphabet to read and to learn. We hope this little workbook will help in doing that.

Working with this workbook

This workbook contains questions to answer at the end of each selection. We hope these questions will help the reader to think and to learn. Some questions require the use of the Bible and a dictionary.

We encourage parents to assist with supplemental work on the lessons in this workbook. For instance, a student could be asked to retell the particular story for the day in proper sequence. This is considered an important skill for understanding events in chronological order. Also, the student could be asked to explain in just a few words the topic or setting of each selection.

Another important skill that can be learned from reading and thinking is drawing conclusions. This is learning facts by figuring out things that may not be said in a story. For instance, if a student reads, "Andy lives on a farm. He helps his parents take care of the animals," the student can conclude that Andy's parents are farmers though it is never specifically stated. As an additional exercise, the student can be asked to draw conclusions from the information presented in the stories.

We hope you enjoy reading this story and doing the exercises.

Chapter 1

"Joe! Joe! Come out! I want to show you something!"

Joe stood up and looked out of the doorway. He wanted to run out of his house to see what his Egyptian friend Pepi had to show him. His birthday was only two days away. "Maybe Pepi has a present for me!" he thought. However, he had to be patient.

Joe sat back down at his father Jacob's feet. Jacob had gathered his wife and children in the family room to speak on a very serious matter.

Joe's younger sister, Lia, knelt on a cushion next to him in front of their father. Their baby brother, Juda, was in his mother's arms behind both of them. Joe turned and smiled at Juda trying to wiggle off his mother's lap, red curls bouncing and big blue eyes twinkling with mischief. Joe noted how much Juda looked like his mother Ruth, although *her* hair was blonde.

Joe and Lia were dark-haired and black-eyed like their father. Joe was proud to look like his father; he was eager also to have a long black wavy beard like Jacob's.

He turned back to look at his father. Joe thought about the special messages his father had given him since his tenth birthday about a year ago. Now he had a little tickle of pleasure that his father's "serious matter" might be about a birthday present. (He had thrown out hints about a colorful bird that could talk!) However, as his father began speaking, all thoughts of his birthday left Joe's mind.

The sun still glared high in the blue Egyptian sky over their home in the city of Goshen (or Ramesses, as the Egyptians called it, after a powerful pharaoh). As Joe's father began talking, he looked intently around at his family seated in the sparsely furnished room. Joe quickly noticed a tenseness in his father's voice. He realized his father was not going to discuss his imminent birthday.

Jacob held a roll of papyrus which he began to open up. "I have written the words of the Lord God on this scroll," he declared.

"Our great leader Moses, to whom the Lord God speaks, called our priests and lawgivers together for a meeting today. Our kinsmen from all the way near the Red Sea attended the meeting."

Jacob paused. His voice became softer. "First, let us pray to the Lord God for mercy on those who oppress us." He bowed his head and his family bowed theirs. He said, "We pray also that the Lord God put forgiveness in our hearts for the Pharaoh Mereneptah and his officers and overseers of the brickyards."

Again Jacob paused; then raising his head, he continued, his voice deepening. "Now, I must tell you, the time of retribution for Egypt has arrived."

"I have written the words of the Lord God on this scroll," he declared.

Chapter 1 – Questions

1. Why did Joe want to see his friend Pepi?_____

    _____

2. Why did he stay in his house? _____

    _____

3. What did Joe think his father was going to talk about?_____

    _____

4. What did Joe want his father to give him for a birthday present? _____

    _____

5. Who was the head of Joe's family? _____

6. What do you think "imminent" most nearly means?
    a) will happen soon   b) great
    c) strange   d) is unlikely to happen

7-8. "Jacob held a roll of papyrus." What is papyrus? What do we have today

    instead of papyrus? _____

    _____

9. From the story, do you think the Pharaoh Mereneptah (pronounced

    Me-re-nep´-tah) was a good ruler or a bad ruler? Why? _____

    _____

    _____

10. Would you like to have lived in Egypt? Why or why not?_____

    _____

    _____

Chapter 2

Joe shivered at hearing his father's words. He remembered well that during the year since his tenth birthday, some terrible things had happened in Egypt, but not in the land of the Israelites, here in Goshen.

Joe's father resumed speaking. "When our great leader Moses first returned to Egypt, he told Pharaoh that the Lord God wanted His people, our Israelite nation, to leave Egypt in order to make a special sacrifice to Him. "You remember, don't you, Joseph, how Moses' brother Aaron had a rod that God turned into a snake, and how by the power of Satan, the Egyptian magicians turned their rods into snakes?"

"Yes, Father," Joe answered, "and then Aaron's snake-rod devoured the magicians' snake-rods!"

"That's correct, Joe. Aaron is one of God's holy men also." Joe's young brow was now wrinkled with worry. "And then later," continued Jacob, "you remember when Pharaoh Mereneptah refused to let us go, and Moses turned all the water of Egypt into blood?

"And you remember that the Lord God sent many more plagues into Egypt to make Pharaoh see He is the God of the Egyptians as well as the Israelites?" Jacob stopped and slowly shook his head in sorrow. "But Pharaoh still refuses to let us leave Egypt."

Joe excitedly spoke now: "Yes, Father, I remember you told us about those awful frogs that came out of the river all over Egypt and how they had a terrible smell."

"Yes, Joseph, but the Egyptian magicians could not make the frogs go away; and even after the Lord God sent the frogs back to the river, Mereneptah would not let us leave Egypt." His voice became lower. "He forced us to make bricks." His voice trailed off and he gazed at his hands.

Then, Joe's mother said softly, "Yes, and then he ordered that no straw should be given to us to make the bricks but we must get our own … oh!" She sounded as if she were about to cry.

The Rod of Aaron Devours the Other Rods (James Tissot)

4

Chapter 2 – Questions

1. Who was the Israelite leader?_____

_____

2. Who was Aaron?_____

_____

3-4. Why did God send the plagues into Egypt? Name two of the plagues.

_____

_____

5. What kind of people do you think the "magicians" were? _____

_____

6. Jacob said that the Egyptians forced him to make bricks, and then he

   looked at his hands. Why did he look at his hands?_____

_____

7. Why did God want His people to leave Egypt? _____

_____

8. Pharaoh persecuted God's people. There have been many evil people
   throughout history who have hated God and persecuted innocent people.
   What do you think Catholics like yourself should do for people like this?

_____

_____

The Plague of Locusts (James Tissot)

Chapter 3

Jacob patted her shoulder. "Dear Ruth! Yes, we have seen much and endured much from the Egyptian tyrants; but of those awful plagues, *we* have endured none in our land of Goshen. We thank our Lord God for this! We have been protected from the terrible biting insects, the swarms of flies, the sickness among the animals, and the horrible sores on the Egyptian people and their animals."

Joe jumped up, exclaiming, "Yes, Father, and you told us about the great hail that came with fire and destroyed everything that was not under cover among the Egyptians!"

Now Lia jumped up, eager to be part of the family discussion. Her little voice almost squeaky with earnestness, she exclaimed, "Father, after the hail came, those scary locusts ate everything that was left after the hail!"

"And that awful darkness that lasted three days," said Joe's mother. In a low voice she added, "Those poor Egyptian people suffered because of their Pharaoh." She sighed, shaking her head.

Jacob tried to soothe his family. "I know, I know." He looked anxiously at Juda, by now sleeping peacefully in his mother's arms. "Ahh! I hope *he* never sees days like these. Still, it is wonderful to see the hand of the Lord God, so powerful, so magnificent, and yet, at the same time showing His infinite love for His people. For, again, *we* did not experience the terrible darkness of those three days or those other plagues; but all this time, the Pharaoh has over and over again broken his word to let us go, and now..." He stopped speaking.

Joe's mother hesitated, and then said, "And now? What now, Jacob?"

At his mother's question, Joe sat down again, drawing his sister Lia down beside him. Though he knew the sun was sizzling everything outside, he felt cold shivers up and down his back. Then, looking up at his father, he echoed his mother's words: "Now, Father?"

"Now, today," said Jacob, "today, Moses gave us the word from the Lord God." Jacob read slowly from the scroll: "God said, 'And I will pass through the land of Egypt that night, and will kill every firstborn in the land of Egypt, both man and beast; and against all the gods of Egypt, I will execute judgments. I am the Lord'."

Jacob stopped speaking. There was a deep silence in the room except for the gentle breathing of the sleeping baby, Juda. Ruth began to moan, rocking her baby back and forth. The realization of the terrible meaning of the Lord's words made Joe stumble to his feet.

Chapter 3 – Questions

1-2. Did Jacob's family suffer from the plagues and darkness? Why or why not?

_____

3. What is a tyrant? _____

4-5. What kinds of insects plagued the Egyptian people? Are these kinds of

insects still alive today? _____

_____

6-7. What terrible fate did God promise the Egyptians? Why did that make

Ruth moan? _____

_____

_____

_____

8. What is another word for "firstborn"? _____

9-10. What did Joe's mother think of the Egyptian people? Did she blame them

or the Pharaoh for the abuses to God's people? _____

_____

The Seventh Plague (John Martin)

Chapter 4

"Father! Father! What about my friend Pepi and his family next door to us?" Joe's voice was urgent.

Lia began to cry. Jacob tried to comfort all of them. Speaking gently, he said, "Remember that our Lord God is our Creator. It is His right to give life and to take it away. Remember that the cries of the Israelites against their oppressors have gone up to God for a very long time. Remember, too, that the Pharaoh has defied the Lord God and broken his promises many times.

"The Lord God is infinitely merciful and patient, but when there is no sorrow for offending Him and no intention of ceasing the offense, it is His right to take action. And though killing the firstborn of the Egyptians seems like a terrible thing, the Lord God thus shows how terrible it is to offend Him. God's justice is perfect and cannot be questioned."

Ruth looked pleadingly at her husband, and with anguish whispered, "Pepi's family has been good to us. They helped us when they saw how you were whipped by the Pharaoh's taskmasters."

Joe saw his father's forehead wrinkle with consternation at Ruth's words. Joe knew his parents loved the family next door and that Pepi's family returned that love. They had shown it many times. For a long time, Pepi's father, Seti, and his mother, Tai, had quietly and unostentatiously helped Jacob and his family. Pepi's parents saw Jacob come home after dark each night, barely able to drag one foot after the other, after working in the Egyptian brickyards since early morning.

Seti was a scribe and an architect for the Pharaoh. He was also an artist and loved to collect beautiful objects. Every so often, when Seti and his family visited Joe's home, Joe noticed how Seti admired some of the golden goblets and dishes on the shelves. Several times Joe heard Seti very casually ask Jacob if he would be willing to part with one or two of them, "for a good price, of course, Jacob," he would say. Though it saddened Jacob to give up his ancestral possessions, he felt more upset at seeing his family go hungry. For the past several months, his pay had been reduced to nearly nothing because he had to buy straw to make bricks, as did all the Israelite men.

Jacob had explained to Joe that he realized his friend Seti was really trying to help him without embarrassing or demeaning him and that he appreciated the offers— and so accepted them. In the same way, Pepi's mother, Tai, had brought over some tasty dish she prepared, saying Ruth would be doing her a favor by taking it because "I just didn't figure out the amounts properly, and it turned out to be too much for us and will just go to waste!"

Typical Egyptian Art

Chapter 4 – Questions

1. Why was Joe concerned about Pepi and his family? _____

    _____

2. What did Jacob say is God's right? _____

    _____

3. What did Ruth think of Pepi's family? _____

    _____

4. Consternation most nearly means:
    a) building
    b) dismay
    c) questioning
    d) pay
    e) helplessness

5. Unostentatiously most nearly means:
    a) boldly
    b) loudly
    c) in a hidden way

6. Where did Jacob work?_____

    _____

7. How did Jacob happen to possess gold dishes?_____

    _____

8. Why did Jacob appreciate Seti's offers? _____

    _____

9-10. Are the crimes of a nation sometimes just the fault of the ruler, and not

    the fault of the common people in the country? Why? _____

    _____

Chapter 5

Jacob was extremely concerned about his friends next door, but he respected and believed what Moses had declared God had said: Every firstborn in the land of Egypt shall die.

Jacob stared into his wife's eyes, her words of anxiety still troubling his heart. Then he said, as he unrolled the scroll slowly from right to left, "Our prophet Moses also told us that God said, 'On the tenth day of this month, let every man take a lamb without blemish by their families and houses. But if the number be less than may suffice to eat the lamb, he shall take unto him his neighbor that joineth to his house, according to the number of souls which may be enough to eat the lamb ... and you shall keep it until the fourteenth day of this month ... and sacrifice it in the evening ... and take the blood thereof and put it upon both the side posts and on the upper door posts of the houses wherein they shall eat it. And they shall eat the flesh that night roasted in the fire, and unleavened bread with bitter herbs.... If there be anything left, you shall burn it with fire.... And thus you shall eat it: you shall gird your loins, and you shall have shoes on your feet, holding staves in your hands, and you shall eat in haste, for it is ... the Passover of the Lord...."

Jacob stopped speaking. For a moment, there was silence. Then Joe's mother said in a trembling voice, "He shall take unto him his neighbor that joineth to his house ..." She was silent.

Nodding his head, Joe's father again read the words of God: "...according to the number of souls which may be enough to eat the lamb."

Hearing these words, Joe began to understand that the Lord God would save his friend Pepi and his family. His heart was pounding as he leaped up, saying, "Father!" but his father was already speaking: "Yes, I believe the family of Seti may join us in our house to consume that lamb on the fourteenth day of this month."

Joe wanted to ask his father a hundred questions, but his father looked so serious that Joe decided just to listen to him tell more of God's words.

Mereneptah, Pharaoh of Egypt

Chapter 5 – Questions

1. Today, under the appearance of unleavened bread, we consume the Body and Blood of Christ. What do we call it? _____

   _____

2. How was it possible that Seti's family could be saved? _____

   _____

3. What did God tell Moses the Israelites should do after they ate the meal?

   _____

4. What were the Israelites told to put on their doorposts? _____

   _____

5. What does "haste" mean? _____

   _____

6. Which sacrament does the "lamb without blemish" represent? _____

   _____

7. What are staves? _____

   _____

8. Why was Joe's heart pounding? _____

   _____

   _____

Picture of Geese from Egyptian Tomb

Chapter 6

Joe's father again read from the scroll: "The Lord God also said, '... the blood of the lamb shall be unto you for a sign in the houses where you shall be; and I shall see the blood and shall pass over you; and the plague shall not be upon you to destroy you, when I shall strike the land of Egypt.'"

Jacob rose and walked slowly around the room, still holding the scroll, and continued speaking: "Moses told us God said, 'The cry of the children of Israel has come unto me and I have seen their affliction,' and that Moses would 'lead the children of Israel, His people, out of Egypt.'"

Jacob paused a moment, looking sadly at his wife. "Ruth, you know how it has been for almost two generations now, for me and my father before me; every day we have struggled and labored as slaves in the clay pits under the whips of the overseers, just to make bricks for more monuments for the Egyptians and their false gods."

Joe's eyes filled with tears as he looked at his father's lined face and roughened hands. He had gone one day to the pits with his mother to take his father a bit of fruit to refresh him. He saw his father among hundreds of other men, some Israelites and others captured in wars. Some were churning the heavy wet clay with their feet while others were mixing straw and clay together and filling trays of brick-shape forms.

The pits stretched out over a large area, almost as big as the river that Joe saw in the distance. Joe recognized some of his father's friends nearby, all striving to dodge the constantly flailing whips of the Egyptian overseers.

Many times, when his father returned home after a grueling day, Joe asked him some question, but his father was too tired to answer. Then Joe would show his anger at the evil brick-masters, but his father always just laid a hand on Joe's shoulder and said, "The Lord knows, son." But now, Joe came back to the present, seeing his father overcome with emotion.

Jacob stopped speaking and sat down, his shoulders hunched. Joe's mother, still holding baby Juda closely, leaned over to Jacob and put an arm around him, saying, "Jacob, the Lord God loves you."

Joe and his sister then quickly moved to their father and leaned their heads against him. The baby began to cry softly. Jacob touched each of them and said, "They have taken almost everything from me—but I still have my darling family."

Joe remembered the gold cups and dishes they used to have—heirlooms treasured by the family and used for prayers and ceremonies—and how they "disappeared," one by one. Joe hugged his father.

Chapter 6 – Questions

1. How did Ruth comfort Jacob? _____

   _____

2. How did Joe and Lia try to comfort Jacob? _____

   _____

3. Why did they comfort Jacob? _____

   _____

4. Joe said that the gold cups and dishes disappeared, one by one. Why do

   you think they disappeared? _____

   _____

5. What is an "heirloom"? _____

   _____

6-7. What were the two most important things in life to Jacob? _____

   _____

8. The story says that Joe showed his anger at the evil brick-masters. Why?

   _____

   _____

9. "Flailing" most nearly means:

   a) falling

   b) hailing

   c) wildly swinging

   d) screaming

Ramesses II, Father of Mereneptah

13

Chapter 7

Just then, Joe heard his friend Pepi calling him again, "Joe! Joe! Where are you? Come outside!"

Joe looked at his father, questioning with his eyes. Jacob said, "Joe, go along and see what your friend wants … And Joe, you may tell his father I shall visit him this evening after dinner, but Joe, don't say anything of what I have just talked about! Just tell him I shall be over later."

Joe replied, "Yes, Father," and he ran outside to his friend.

"Pepi, I was busy so I couldn't come out right away. What did you want to show me?"

Pepi had a flat, square-shaped wooden box in his hands. "I just couldn't wait for your birthday, Joe!" he said, giving the box to Joe.

Joe smiled widely, his dark eyes bright with anticipation. The boys sat down on the back step of Joe's house as he looked at the box. It was golden-brown olive wood, so polished that Joe could see his face in it. The outside of the lid had some odd-looking marks painted in green on it. "That's your name in Egyptian, Joe," said Pepi, pointing to the center of the lid.

"That's *my* name in Egyptian!" exclaimed Pepi, as he pointed to the lower right corner of the lid.

There were intricately designed bright brass hinges on one side of the box, and an equally elaborate brass hook-and-eye on the other. Joe carefully released the hook and raised the lid.

The bottom inside of the box was lined with a glistening, sky-blue material. Joe rubbed his fingers on it, saying, "It looks like a mantle my mother used to have!" Resting on the lining, in little places shaped especially for each piece, were checker pieces in four rows.

The light pieces were carved ivory, and the dark pieces were carved from a beautiful dark green stone.

The checkerboard was inside the lid, inlaid with shiny wood squares painted black and red, outlined with gold. It was really beautiful, Joe thought.

Joe could hardly find words to thank his friend. Pepi was bubbling over with pleasure at seeing Joe's reaction to the extraordinary gift.

"Joe, now you and I can play our own games together!" Both boys laughed at the prospect, because Pepi had been borrowing his father's checkers for their games and—since it was his father's favorite game that he played almost every evening with Joe's father—they did not get to play as much as they wanted!

"Pepi, come into my house with me! I want to show this to my mother and father." So they both ran into Joe's house.

"That's your name in ancient Egyptian, Joe," said Pepi, pointing to the center of the lid.

Chapter 7 – Questions

1-2. Why did Jacob want to talk to Pepi's father? Why do you think Jacob did not want Joe to mention anything about Moses' words right away?

_____

_____

_____

3. What does "intricately" mean? Look in the dictionary for the proper

pronunciation. _____

_____

4-5. What are some other words for "anticipation"? _____

_____

6. Of what were the checker pieces made?_____

_____

7-8. With what was the bottom inside of the box lined? What rested on this lining?

_____

_____

9-10. At the beginning of this chapter, Jacob asked Joe to do something. What

was it? Did Joe remember to do it? _____

_____

Tomb Painting of Trees and Bushes

16

Chapter 8

Joe's parents even more appreciated Pepi's gift, because they could see its great value as well as its beauty. The whole family examined the set and thanked Pepi profusely for such a beautiful gift.

Finally, Joe's father said, "Joe, did Pepi's father say that I could visit him after supper this evening?"

"Oh, Father! I forgot to ask! When I saw this great checker set—I'm sorry, Father!" Joe hesitated. He was chagrined at forgetting his father's request.

"That's understandable. Don't worry." Turning to Pepi, Joe's father said, "I should very much appreciate your telling your father that I shall be over later to see him, if it is convenient."

So Joe and Pepi ran out of the house, Joe still carrying his gift because he also wanted to say thank you to Pepi's mother and father.

"Your mom and dad have been so nice to our family," said Joe as he trotted along beside Pepi.

Pepi nodded. "Yes, I guess it's because they all like the same things."

"Just like us, huh?" said Joe, smiling.

"Yeah, I guess so—well," he opened his front door, "c'mon in!" Pepi felt a little awkward at compliments, but he really did feel good when doing something nice for somebody else, and especially for Joe, whom he considered his best friend "because he always goes along with whatever I want to do!" he said to himself, "and he's always smiling." He knew, too, that his family liked Joe almost as much as he did.

So, as they stepped into the house, both boys were glowing in appreciation, one from receiving and the other from giving.

Chapter 8 – Questions

1. What does "profusely" mean? _____

    _____

2. What did Joe's family think of the checker set? _____

    _____

3-4. St. Francis of Assisi said that it is better to give than receive. Who else in the story thinks this saying is true? What do you think? _____

    _____

    _____

5. Pepi felt awkward receiving compliments. Why? _____

    _____

6. Whom else did Joe want to thank for the checker set?_____

    _____

7. What is another word for "beautiful"? _____

8. How did Jacob show his kindness to his son?_____

    _____

9. How is the word "glowing" used in this chapter?_____

    _____

10. "Chagrined" most nearly means:

    a) angry

    b) happy

    c) silly

    d) upset

Chapter 9

Joe had been in Pepi's house many times. However, he had peeked only once into a certain room. It was a special room for Pepi's family. This made Joe very curious to see inside the room. It occurred to Joe that he might never see the room at all if they were all going to leave Egypt.

So, now, entering Pepi's house, he decided to ask Tai, Pepi's mother, if he could go into the room. First, though, he thanked Seti and Tai for the wonderful gift of checkers, also saying how much his parents appreciated it. Tai accepted his thanks graciously and then invited Joe to stay for a game with Pepi.

"Thank you very much," said Joe, "but—could you—would you let me—may I—?" and Joe stopped in confusion.

"What is it, Joe?" asked Seti, smiling kindly.

Joe got up his courage. "You have that very special room, and I've peeked in it only once, and there are some beautiful things there, and I wish I could see them closely and—" he stopped again.

Tai looked at Seti, who nodded and said, "We are glad that you like those things in that room, Joe. This just might be a good time for you to see them again. Go ahead; Pepi will show you the room. Take your time." He gestured the boys out.

The house was of brick as Joe's was, but it was laid out in the shape of an E, whereas Joe's was a two-story rectangular block. Pepi's house also had more rooms.

"My father is an architect besides being a scribe," said Pepi, "and so were his father and grandfather and great-grandfather, back twenty-three generations!"

"That's the way with *my* father, too," said Joe. "I don't know exactly how many generations it could be, but I know it was about four hundred and thirty years ago that our great patriarch Joseph brought his family and all the Israelites here to Goshen. I am a descendant of Joseph."

"And that's why you're named after him?" asked Pepi. "Yes, but I think it was Joseph my grandfather who added on to our house," said Joe.

The Great Sphinx at Giza, Egypt

Chapter 9 – Questions

1. What does "graciously" mean? _____

   _____

2-3. Why did Joe want to see the special room? Why did he want to see it soon?

   _____

   _____

4. How did Joe show his good manners? _____

   _____

5-6. Who do you think is the head of Pepi's house? Why? _____

   _____

7. How was Pepi's house different from Joe's? _____

   _____

8. After whom was Joe named? _____

   _____

9. What is a patriarch? _____

   _____

10. What kind of job do you think Pepi will have when he grows up? _____

   _____

20

Chapter 10

"One of my great-great-grandfathers built our house," said Pepi, "but it has been added onto by my grandfather and my father. In the beginning, it was just this one wing where the room is that you want to see. Here it is."

By this time they had arrived at the special prayer room.

"This is in the center of our house," said Pepi in a whisper. "My ancestor built this wing first."

Joe felt this room was so mysterious that his heart pounded as Pepi pulled aside the heavy curtain in the doorway. "Why do I feel this way?" said Joe to himself. Then he remembered when he had peeked into this room before, he had seen strange figures in the semidarkness, with large eyes staring at him.

As Pepi's dark hand reached across the golden curtain to pull it aside for Joe, it added to Joe's feeling of mystery.

Pepi gestured to Joe to go in. The sun was low in the sky but still bright as Joe cautiously entered the room, but the room was quite dim, as it had only one small opening slit in the wall near the ceiling. It was otherwise lighted by small oil lamps. There were just three, hanging from bronze bars protruding from the walls. Their flickering light, however, could not conceal the brightness of gold covering two large cases standing against the wall. They were the figures Joe had seen before when he peeked in.

"My mother's father and my father's mother are in those cases," Pepi said in a whisper. "We don't talk out loud here, out of reverence for the dead," he added.

Joe nodded and stepped closer to the cases. They were made of wood and followed the outline of a human figure, as if a person were standing at attention. The head area had what looked like a hood on it, with the face carved and painted below it.

"The man who makes those tries to make the face look like the person who died," whispered Pepi. Joe noticed the painted eyes especially, because they were outlined in black, so they seemed to stare at Joe.

"I guess they are what made me nervous before!" he whispered to Pepi with a smile.

"My mother's father and my father's mother are in those cases," Pepi said in a whisper.

Chapter 10 – Questions

1. Where was the "special" room?_____

    _____

2. Did it have a door?_____

    _____

3. Why did the boys whisper? _____

    _____

4. What does "flickering" mean? _____

    _____

5. What does "protruding" mean?_____

    _____

6. What is "reverence"?_____

    _____

7. Was the room well lit? How do you know?_____

    _____

8. Why did Joe's heart pound as Pepi pulled aside the curtain in the doorway?

    _____

    _____

9. How many oil lamps were in the room? _____

10. What were the faces on the wooden body cases carved to resemble? _____

    _____

Burial Case

23

Chapter 11

All kinds of shapes were carved in the wood surface: birds with their plumage in gold, red and blue; various animals, such as leopards, crocodiles, and hippopotamuses; and trees and bushes—all in bright blues, reds, greens, and yellows, with golden trim outlining everything. All these surrounded a panel that extended up and down the front of the cases. Within the panel were vertical rows of tiny black shapes, dots, and bird figures.

"Those little black figures are Egyptian writing, like on your new checker box," whispered Pepi. "They tell the story of the things the dead person did while alive," he added.

"You remember that my ancestors were architects, right?" Pepi asked. "Yes," nodded Joe. "So, look here, and here, and there," explained Pepi, pointing to little human figures bending over stones and measuring sticks on the case of his grandfather.

Joe was fascinated with these picture stories. After studying them for a while, he finally turned to look at the other things in the room.

He noticed several small granite columns on which were golden figures. Joe felt uneasy, as he realized that they were the images of false gods. Suddenly, the words of Moses, which Joe had learned from his father, Jacob, came into his mind:

"Thou shalt fear the Lord thy God, and shalt serve Him only." (See Deuteronomy 6:13, where God eventually inspired Moses to write down these words.)

"Do you ... worship these statues?" Joe asked meekly.

Pepi explained that the Egyptians did not worship the statues themselves, but the gods that they represented.

Joe's heart began pounding again, this time because he wanted so much to tell Pepi about the True Lord God. Joe knew that worshiping false gods offended God very much, and he longed to tell Pepi that, too. However, he decided to tell his father about the Egyptian beliefs first, "because Father will know what to say better than I," Joe thought. So, instead, he just whispered quietly, "We believe in *one* God," and he repeated the words of Moses in his mind several times:

"Thou shalt fear the Lord thy God, and shalt serve Him only."

Joe slowly made a motion toward the curtain where they first entered the room, and Pepi walked over and politely opened it for him. As they walked out of the dimly lit room, Pepi resumed speaking.

"My father said that *his* grandfather on his father's side was very important in the court of the Pharaoh at that time; so when he died, there was a huge procession of people who carried the sarcophagus on a golden wagon covered with flowers down to the river; and then they put it on a barge covered with flowers and sang sad songs."

Chapter 11 – Questions

1. What kinds of pictures were on the cases? _____

_____

2. From the text, tell about Egyptian funeral traditions._____

_____

3. What is "plumage"? _____

_____

4. What did the Egyptian writing look like? Can you think of any other
   language used today in the Far East that uses drawings and letters to
   represent ideas? _____

_____

5. How is our writing different from Egyptian writing? _____

_____

6. What words of Moses came into Joe's mind when he saw the images of the
   false gods? _____

_____

7. According to Pepi, did the Egyptians actually worship their statues?

_____

8-9. Joe wanted to tell Pepi about his faith in the One True God. Why did he
   want to wait for his father to talk to Pepi and his family instead? Have
   you ever wanted to talk to a non-Catholic friend about your Catholic
   Faith? What should we do in times when we want to communicate our
   faith to another? Should we pray to the Holy Spirit for wisdom?

_____

_____

_____

10. Why do you think Joe kept repeating in his mind the words of Moses about
    fearing God and serving Him only? _____

_____

Chapter 12

"What's a sarcophagus?" interrupted Joe.

"That's the big case which they put the body case into," answered Pepi. "The dead are placed in the body case first, and then they are placed in the sarcophagus. A sarcophagus is shaped like the body case and is usually all covered with gold and painted like the cases I showed you in our special room," said Pepi.

"There was a second barge, too, that followed the body barge. All the women of the family went in that, singing sad songs about my father's grandfather."

"But where did they go?" asked Joe.

"They went down south along the river," answered Pepi. "There are pyramids down there. My father's grandfather was put in one of those," said Pepi with a little sound of pride in his voice. "The great Pharaoh I was named after is buried in the same area, in a pyramid near the city he founded, the City of Pepi. He reigned over Egypt for 95 years," added Pepi.

"That sure is a long time! He must have been a very old man when he died!" said Joe.

"He became king when he was only six years old," said Pepi. "He conquered all the tribes from where the River Nile starts up in the mountains down to the Red Sea."

"But that was a long time ago, wasn't it?" said Joe.

"Yes, and the last Pharaohs have not been very good for Egypt, my father says, because they take so much from the people that—well—that's why we have our grandparents here. Hardly anybody can afford a big funeral or bury their dead in a pyramid anymore. Nearly everyone has their dead relatives at home with them now." Pepi shook his head sadly.

"Well, it's getting near dinner time," said Joe. Joe was remembering about the impending meeting of his father with Pepi's father. "Thanks for showing me your special room and telling me about your family and everything."

As they began walking away from Pepi's house, he turned around and cheerfully exclaimed: "Thanks again for that great checker set, Pepi!"

Joe returned home and told his father that Pepi's father would be glad to see him later. Then he opened his gift again, took out every piece, examined it carefully, and placed it in game position on the checkerboard. He was ready for a game.

Suddenly Joe remembered what his father had told his family earlier. He began to wonder if he would ever again play checkers with Pepi.

Chapter 12 – Questions

1. What was the difference between the funerals of a very important Egyptian and one not so important? _____

   _____

2. What is a sarcophagus? _____

   _____

3-4. What are pyramids? Where are they? _____

   _____

   _____

5-6. Ask your parent to help you look up the great pyramid of Cheops in an encyclopedia or try to find a book on pyramids at the library. Write about Cheops or another pyramid. _____

   _____

   _____

   _____

   _____

7. What does "impending" mean? _____

   _____

8. Why did Joe wonder if he would ever play checkers again with Pepi?

   _____

9. After whom was Pepi named? _____

   _____

10. How old was the Pharaoh Pepi when he became king? How old was he when he died? _____

   _____

Chapter 13

Dinner time was unusually quiet for Joe's family that evening. His father said more prayers than usual at the beginning of the meal, but after that, only baby Juda clamoring for more food and his mother's softly soothing voice were heard. Even Lia was not doing her usual jabbering, Joe noticed. She just played quietly with her doll.

The meal was shorter than usual, too, because Joe's father excused himself from the table very soon and told his family he was going over to see his friend Seti.

Joe was barely able to wait until his mother put Juda and Lia to bed before speaking to her.

"Mother, Father said that on the tenth day of this month we must take a lamb and …"

Ruth interrupted him, "Joe, dear, the Lord God is doing great things for us, and your father will see that everything is done in good order and on time. So, trust in the Lord and your father! But we must pray that our friends next door will see that God is giving them a chance to be saved with us."

"I will, Mother," said Joe, "and I will pray for our family too, but Mother, please …" and his voice became strained so that his mother turned sharply to look at him. "Please, Mother, may I stay up until Father comes back home? I want to know if Pepi's father will say they'll come to our house to eat the lamb. Please, Mother?"

Joe's mother ruffled his hair, saying, "Of course, Joe—we'll wait together." She hugged him tenderly.

"Why don't you do a little of your written homework while you are waiting? It will rest your mind a little," she urged.

"Yes, Mother, I will," answered Joe. It was hard for him to keep his mind on his schoolwork.

Statue of Scribe

Chapter 13 – Questions

1. Why was dinner unusual that evening? _____

   _____

2. Why was Joe interested in the tenth day of the month? _____

   _____

3. What did Joe's mother say that showed Joe's father was the head of

   the house? _____

   _____

4. Why did Ruth and Joe want to pray? _____

   _____

5. Why did Ruth allow Joe to stay up later than usual?_____

   _____

6. How did Joe show his obedience?_____

   _____

7. Why was it hard for Joe to keep his mind on his school work?

   _____

   _____

8. What does "ruffled" mean? _____

   _____

Chapter 14

The awesome glory of moon and stars filled the dark dome of the night as Jacob arrived home from Pepi's house, and he offered a prayer of thanks to the Lord God for His beautiful creation of night.

On entering his home, Jacob saw Joe half asleep in his chair, his papyrus and stylus in his lap. Ruth came quickly to greet Jacob. Joe, rubbing his eyes, ran to greet his father too. "Father—?"

Jacob embraced them and said, "Pepi's whole family is coming over tomorrow night to talk about our plans. Seti could not say right away what they would do because he had to consult with Tai.

"So we have to wait until tomorrow night for their answer. We still have over a week to plan for the lamb, so we can wait."

Ruth asked, "So they will come over tomorrow after dinner—*all* of them?"

"Yes. Seti and Tai and Pepi and the baby Hatasu. They will discuss the words of the Lord God at their home and then come over right after dinner so that they'll have time to get the children to bed afterward." Joe had never seen his father quite so stirred up except maybe the day Juda was born, but this was different excitement. It was mostly anxiety. Joe realized he felt the same way. Even so, now his eyes were beginning to droop again, so he put away his writing things, kissed his parents good night, picked up his birthday gift, and started up to bed.

However, he couldn't help thinking that, as each step took him closer to his room, it was also taking him closer to tomorrow night's meeting and a fateful decision.

Suddenly, he did not feel sleepy at all.

Chapter 14 – Questions

1. What is papyrus? _____

   _____

2. What is a stylus?

   _____

3. Why was Jacob excited? _____

   _____

   _____

4. What other time excited him? _____

   _____

5. What was different about the excitement referred to in question 3
   compared to the excitement referred to in question 4? _____

   _____

   _____

6. What did Jacob mean when he said "plan for the lamb"? _____

   _____

7. Why do you think *all* of Seti's family would be coming to Joe's house?

   _____

8. Joe was anxious for his friends. Write the sentence in the story that
   indicates this.

   _____

   _____

   _____

9. Why could Seti not make his decision right away? _____

   _____

   _____

10. Why did Joe suddenly not feel sleepy? _____

    _____

    _____

31

Chapter 15

Joe was very tired, though, and that night he was extra grateful for the comfortable bed his parents had provided him. He fell asleep thinking how much he liked his room. Suddenly, it was morning. The sun was shining in his face, the birds were singing their morning joy to their Creator, and the lazy palms rustled softly in the new dawn's breeze. His room was in the corner of his house. There were slits near the ceiling on the south wall, and in the east wall was a large doorway to a porch just outside his room. Pushing aside the gauze curtain covering the doorway, Joe stepped out to sniff the morning air. He saw an ibis nest in a nearby olive tree, with a chick in it, fluttering its wings and squawking for its breakfast.

Past the trees in the distance, he saw the waters of a branch of the Nile, reflecting the bright azure sky. To the south, he saw a mass of dark green rising to meet the cloudless roof of the heavens. Joe had never been that far away from home, but his father had told him of the land beyond the hills where there were mountains whose gorges were filled with glaciers and their tops covered with snow.

"That is where most of our water comes from," Joe's father had told him. "Some comes from another mountain range far to the southeast, but the most interesting part of that land is where the water from the glaciers tumbles down the rocks and flows through swampy land and muddy morasses."

"It must be cold up in those mountains," said Joe as he wiped some perspiration from his brow.

Drinking Vessel in the Shape of a Fish

Jacob laughed. "Cold enough that I even had a piece of frozen water that a friend brought me! But down below on the other side of the mountains, it's as hot as it is here. There are thick jungles that a man can't get through without cutting his way," Jacob added. "There are huge thickets of tamarisks, sycamores, and bamboo forests that the sun never gets through."

"I sure wouldn't want to live *there*," said Joe. "I *love* the sun!"

His father laughed. "You might want to live where the forest thins out near water places for animals!"

"What animals?" asked Joe, his eyes lighting up.

"Why, all kinds!" said Jacob. "They come out of the forest and down through the reeds on the muddy banks—zebras, antelopes—even elephants! You should see those baby elephants—how they hang onto their mother's tails with their little trunks!"

Chapter 15 – Questions

1. Where does the water of Egypt come from?_____

   _____

2. What is "gauze"? _____

   _____

3. What bird did Joe see? _____

   _____

4. What is a glacier? _____

   _____

5. What is a "gorge"? In what other way can the word "gorge" be used?

   _____

   _____

6. Where did Joe's father think Joe might like to live?_____

   _____

7. What is a morass? _____

   _____

8. What kinds of animals inhabited the jungle? _____

   _____

9-10. Why didn't Joe want to live in the jungle? What did Joe like about

   the jungle?_____

   _____

   _____

Chapter 16

The sun burning on Joe's face brought him out of his reverie about the animals. He turned from the porch and into the shade of his room.

Looking around, he thought, "I really love this room!" The room was big enough for his bed, with a canopy and gauze hangings (to keep out flying insects); his tall cabinet, where he hung his clothes; two small wooden stools; a chair; and a small table. On the table, which Joe now approached, were a clay water pitcher and basin, as well as a bowl of sand and another of salt. After cleansing with these, he dipped his finger into a little jar of oil and then into two bowls of powder, one green and one black, and making a little paste, he smeared it under his eyes so that the sun's glare would not burn them.

He had plenty of room in which to play with his cat, Dan, who still slept in his basket in a corner. Dan was white, like his basket, which had a cushion that was green like his eyes. Joe tried to wake up Dan, rubbing his fur the wrong way, but Dan only half opened one eye, choosing to ignore Joe. After all, he had been out all night chasing other cats!

So Joe gave up on Dan and went out on his porch again. Since the porch was on the second floor and ran across the whole front of the house, it gave Joe a great view of the road and other houses—like his friend Pepi's home, which was the next house, about a hundred feet away. The porch was supported by four graceful granite columns on which, after the manner of the Egyptians, Joe's family's names were carved. Thus, a visitor could read his family's history from the time they first arrived in Goshen, about 430 years before! Important deeds they had accomplished were also recorded in the granite.

Joe's family descended from the great patriarch Joseph, for whom Joe was named. When Joseph brought his family into Egypt, the Pharaoh Ahmosis assigned them the beautiful land of Goshen in which to live, in the delta of the Nile. Joe's home was built at that time. Joe's ancestors, who had all been scribes, had occupied this same home from the time the great Joseph was an official of the Pharaoh's government and a trusted friend of Pharaoh Ahmosis.

The house was very impressive, and Joe looked at it proudly every day. He thanked God every day, too, for letting him belong to a family of such illustrious ancestors. He felt he had an obligation to live up to their ideals.

Egyptian Dagger

The sun burning on Joe's face brought him out of his reverie about the animals.

Chapter 16 – Questions

1. Why was Joe happy with his room? _____

   _____

2. What was special about the columns in front of Joe's house?_____

   _____

3. Did Joe have a pet? What kind of pet? _____

   _____

4. How long had the Israelites been in Egypt when Joe lived there?

   _____

5-6. Where did Joe's family live? Near what river did they live? _____

   _____

7. What did Joe think of his house?_____

   _____

8. What does "illustrious" mean? _____

   _____

9. Joe felt an obligation to live up to his ancestors' ideals. What do you think he meant? (Which of the Ten Commandments indicates this obligation?)

   _____

   _____

   _____

10. How did Joe's family come to live in Goshen?_____

   _____

   _____

Chapter 17

In the next century after Joe's house was built, an ancestor of Pepi acquired a piece of the property adjacent to Joe's house and constructed a home there, so the two families remained friends for many generations. They were often interested in many of the same things—family traditions, history, art, painting, architecture, and sculpture—and they were always kind and respectful toward each other.

Joe finished dressing and then knelt by his bed to say his morning prayers. "Please, Lord God, let Pepi and his family be saved!"

Then he went to his desk where he had left his new checkers game the night before. "I hope Pepi can play a game with me today," he thought. He ran downstairs to have a quick breakfast and then go see his friend.

The fountain and pool looked so inviting when he passed the open doorway at the back of his house that he decided to jump in the refreshing water first. He carefully doffed his tunic, laying it neatly on a bench. Then he jumped as hard as he could into the pool, making a big splash and gyrating around, pretending to be a crocodile.

Just then his mother called, "Joseph, come have your breakfast now! Pepi's family is coming over this evening, and you must have your lessons done before they come. The sun is very high in the sky already!"

"All right, Mother," answered Joe. He pulled himself out of the water and quickly donned his tunic. He had been so excited about his birthday present that he had forgotten his lessons, but he really did like his studies, particularly because he had the special attention of his mother or father all to himself when they instructed him.

So, Joe had a good-all-over feeling as he hurried into his house for the lessons. Besides, he was eager to tell his mother Pepi's story about his family.

Bedroom Furniture

37

Chapter 17 – Questions

1. Did Joe live near Pepi?_____

_____

2. Why did the families become good friends?_____

_____

_____

3. What in the story would make you think it was a warm day? _____

_____

4. What does "doffed" mean? _____

_____

5. What does "gyrating" mean?_____

_____

6. Where did Joe go to school?_____

_____

7. What did Joe pray to God for? (Do you ever pray for your friends?)

_____

_____

8. What did Joe decide to do before eating breakfast?_____

_____

9-10. As Joe hurried into the house, what was he eager to tell his mother? Why

do you think he was so eager? _____

_____

_____

Chapter 18

Joe hurried through breakfast and gathered up his writing tools and papyrus roll, along with another roll of papyrus that was covered with writing, his lesson for the day. The roll was about 10 inches wide, and 5 feet long when unrolled.

Joe stretched out on his stomach on the cool stones of the family room floor. He used a red jasper stone to smooth the rough papyrus so he could write on it. He also set up two jars of ink: red for capitals, and black. His mother Ruth came in and sat down on a chair nearby. A little ringlet of her blond hair had ventured out from under her white mantle. Joe thought, "How pretty she is!" Her pale blue tunic reached to her feet. She wore a narrow pink sash with a little gold tassel—a small remnant of her family's former affluence. The color of her clothing set off the soft beauty of her face. She had bright blue eyes, a wide forehead, and slightly dark eyebrows arched with interest in those around her. Her mouth was small and gently defined. Her nose was straight, delicately proportioned to the shape of her face. Her complexion was slightly ruddy but still fair.

Ruth's voice interrupted Joe's contemplation of his mother's beauty.

"Now, Joseph, you know the history of our nation of Israelites pretty well, thanks to your father writing it all down for us on these scrolls.

"But for your lesson today I want you to write about the Will of God, particularly where it concerns how our family came to live in Egypt.

"Our great patriarch, Joseph, for whom you are named," and his mother smiled into Joseph's earnest eyes, "became the governor of the whole land of Egypt under the Pharaoh."

"How did that happen, Mother?" asked Joe.

"Because of a dream!" she answered.

"I dream every night, Mother!" laughed Joe. "Sometimes I am flying over the palm trees! Sometimes I am chasing a crocodile!"

Joe's mother smiled.

"This dream was not quite like yours, Joseph. You remember that the Pharaoh Ahmosis was having a certain dream night after night, and so he realized that it really was a serious message for him, but none of his priests could explain it. Finally, Joseph interpreted the dream for him. Do you remember what you read about it, Joseph?" asked Ruth.

"Yes! It was a warning from God about what He was going to do—that He was going to make corn and wheat grow abundantly for seven years all over the land, but after that would be a terrible famine of seven years all over the land—even Egypt!" Joe answered eagerly. He always felt excited when talking about his ancestor Joseph. "You have the same blood!" Ruth had told him when he was younger. "In fact, we are all descended from Noah's son, Shem," she had added, "so we call ourselves Semites."

Chapter 18 – Questions

1. From reading the story, what do you think "affluence" means?_____

   _____

2. What assignment did Joe's mother give him?_____

   _____

3. How did Joseph become the governor of the whole land of Egypt? _____

   _____

   _____

4. From whom did Joseph's family descend? _____

   _____

5. Read about Joseph: Genesis 41:37-57 and answer the following questions:

   What is a "famine"?_____

   _____

6. How old was Joseph when he began to serve the King of Egypt? _____

7. How much grain does the Bible say was produced during the times of plenty?

   _____

Joseph Explains the Dreams of Pharaoh (Antonio del Castillo y Saavedra)

Chapter 19

Ruth spoke again. "And where were Joseph's father, Jacob, his brothers and their families at the time?"

"They were in Canaan!" answered Joe. "How far away is Canaan?"

"You can understand the distance better if you know how long it takes to travel there," answered Ruth. "A large caravan such as Jacob's—they brought all their property, supplies, and herds of animals along with them—must have taken close to two weeks."

"But, before *they* all came, Joseph's brothers came by themselves to buy wheat for their families from Egypt. You see, only Egypt had wheat, because Egypt had stored their wheat during seven years of big harvests, as a result of Joseph's interpretation of the dream of the Pharaoh Ahmosis.

"Joseph, can you see how God brought good out of something evil? Do you remember how Joseph's brothers sold him into slavery to the Egyptians because they were jealous of their father's special attention to him? But God raised Joseph to great importance in Egypt and he saved Joseph's family from starvation. Joseph was God's prophet and gave us a great lesson in forgiveness when he forgave his brothers. Our nation enjoyed some years of prosperity because of Joseph's forgiveness," declared Ruth.

Then Joe remembered his father's words of the night before: "Remember that the cries of the Israelites against their oppressors have gone up to God for a very long time."

"But, mother, now it is different," said Joe.

"Now, again, it is the Lord God who directs our people," said Ruth. She leaned toward Joe, saying in a determined manner, "Joseph, write these words." Joe picked up his rush pen, dipped it in the black ink, and spread the papyrus roll on a large wooden slab, which he held upright on his lap as he sat cross-legged on the floor.

"I want to live all the days of my life according to the Will of God," said Joe's mother.

Joe carefully wrote the words in Hebrew on the scroll. His parents had taught him how to write, and his father was already beginning to teach him how to write in Egyptian also. Joe already could speak Egyptian as well as Hebrew because of his family's friendship with Pepi's family.

Joe finished writing. Ruth spoke again: "If you follow those words all your life, Joseph, you will surely see the Lord God at the end, and you will be following the words of the prophet Joseph."

"I want to live all the days of my life according to the Will of God," said Joe's mother.

Chapter 19 – Questions

1. What language could Joe speak besides Hebrew? _____

2. Write the sentence that Joe's mother told him to write. What do you think it means? _____

   _____

3. What did Joe's mother say would happen to Joe if he followed the words of Joseph the prophet? _____

   _____

4-5. How did the patriarch Joseph respond to his brothers for their evil act to him?

   _____

   What was that evil act? _____

   _____

6. How did God bring something good out of something evil?

   _____

   _____

7. According to Ruth, how far away was the land of Canaan? _____

   _____

8. Why did Egypt have wheat during the great famine? _____

   _____

   _____

9. What is a slab? _____

10. For some years, what did the Hebrews enjoy because of Joseph's act of forgiving his brothers?

   _____

   _____

Chapter 20

"You see," Ruth continued, "when Joseph perceived his brothers were afraid of what he would do to them for selling him into slavery, he told them, according to the words your father's ancestors wrote, 'Be not afraid, and let it not seem a hard case that you sold me into these countries; for God sent me before you into Egypt for your preservation. For it is two years since the famine began to be upon the land, and five years more remain, wherein there can be no plowing or reaping.

'And God sent me before you that you may be preserved upon the Earth, and may have food to live.'"

Ruth hesitated and then said, "Now, Joseph, here are the prophet Joseph's words that you must remember most of all: 'Not by your counsel was I sent hither, but by the Will of God.'

"You see, Joseph, don't you, how our family of Israelites was saved from starvation and death by the Will of God, by a man used by God—our great prophet Joseph?"

Joe nodded.

"Now, in these days," Ruth continued, "the great family of Israelites has been suffering from the Egyptian Pharaohs, especially the present one, Mereneptah."

Joe gazed at his mother, recalling not only his father's suffering and deprivation, but also that of his many cousins and their families who lived throughout Goshen.

In the last few years, even some Egyptian families in Goshen had begun acting cruelly to the Israelites, but Pepi's family had continued to be friendly to Joe and his family.

"Joseph," Ruth said, "now the Lord God is using another man to save the great family of Israelites, our great leader Moses. It was by God's Will, through the hand of Moses, that all those terrible plagues fell on the Egyptians because Pharaoh would not let us go out of this land to sacrifice to the Lord God."

Joe's mother bowed her head, then looked at him and smiled.

"Now it is the Will of God that Moses lead the Israelites out of Egypt to save us from more suffering and death."

Joe said huskily, "That is what Father was telling us about yesterday, wasn't it, Mother?"

"Yes, Joseph, and we must get ready to carry out the Will of God."

Chapter 20 – Questions

1. What does "perceived" mean? _____

   _____

2. What was the name of the Pharaoh who ruled when Joe lived? _____

   _____

3. What does "deprivation" mean in the story? _____

   _____

4-5. How were the Egyptian families treating the Israelites? How did Pepi's

   family treat the Israelites? _____

   _____

   _____

6. Whom did God choose to save the Israelites? _____

   _____

7-8. Why did God send the plagues to Egypt? What was being fulfilled by this?

   _____

   _____

   _____

9. What does "huskily" mean? _____

   _____

10. Why did God want Moses to lead the Israelites out of Egypt? _____

   _____

   _____

Chapter 21

After the lesson with his mother, Joe decided he would not procrastinate, so he finished his assignment right away. He knew he would be permitted to be present when Pepi and his family came over after dinner, and he did not want his work to be still undone.

When he finished, he started to put his writing materials away, but then the thought came to him to write down the events of the past few months. After all, his own father was a scribe for the Israelites. "So why not me?" he thought.

Joe remembered, however, his father telling him about a career as an artist, since the Egyptians were always commissioning artists to decorate the walls of their houses, and especially their tombs.

"We have a wonderful art school right here in Goshen," Jacob had said. "It was founded in ancient times, when Goshen was called Hat Waret. It is so good that people have gone there to learn art down to this day.

"The artists who painted our home," Jacob continued, "and designed Pepi's, came from that school when Ahmosis was Pharaoh. They also helped Pharaoh Ramesses make this city beautiful with temples and paintings. That's why the Egyptians now call Goshen Ramesses in honor of the Pharaoh. They designed our garden and pool, too."

"How does the water get into our pool, Father?" Joe had asked.

"Well, the artists took many clay pots, knocked out their bottoms, and cemented them together between our well and our pool. So the water flows in from the well and drains out the bottom through other underground pipes. Simple but ingenious!" Joe and his father had both laughed.

Now, though, Joe was determined to try to be a scribe. He did not know if his father had done much writing in the last few months during the terrible plagues, because of having to work overtime in the brickyards and clay pits.

Joe had no personal experience of the plagues, because they had not occurred in Goshen. Though Goshen was *in* the land of Egypt, it was not *of* it. God called the Israelites, "His people," and so they were not subjected to the plagues.

Joe knew about the plagues from his father, who was in the Israelite assemblies when Moses reported them after his visits to the Pharaoh Mereneptah.

Joe had just finished writing about Aaron's rod turning into a snake when his mother called him to dinner.

Joe put away his stylus (writing instrument), thinking, "The Pharaoh is a snake himself! One of those poisonous snakes!"

Chapter 21 – Questions

1. "Procrastinate" most nearly means:

   a) delay

   b) object

   c) lie

2-3. Why did Joe think he could be a writer? What were the Israelite writers called? _____

   _____

   _____

4. Did Joe want to be a scribe? _____

   _____

5. Why did Joe consider it important to write down the story of the plagues?

   _____

   _____

6. How did water get into Joe's pool?_____

   _____

7. What does "ingenious" mean?_____

   _____

8. What does "commissioning" mean? _____

   _____

9. What did Joe think of the Pharaoh? _____

   _____

10. What did Christ say that Christians should do to their enemies? (For some help, turn to Luke 6:27-36 in your Bible.) _____

   _____

Chapter 22

Dinner was very brief because everyone anticipated Pepi's family's visit. Joe's mom had cooked his favorite dish of lamb. Joe had smelled the savory scent of the succulent dish while he was doing his lesson. Even so, Joe now gulped it down, so eager was he to hear what Pepi's family would say about the impending departure from Egypt.

Joe thought his baby brother Juda would *never* finish *his* dinner. He kept waving his arms around, spilling his food, and making such a general mess of himself that his mother had to clean him up three times!

The family had just barely settled down after the meal when a knock came at the door. They all stood up. Joe ran and opened the door. There stood Pepi's father Seti and his family.

"Come in! Come in, my dear Seti," said Joe's father, bowing to his friend. "All, please come in." He smiled graciously at Tai and the children.

"Thank you, Jacob," said Seti.

Joe admired Seti's handsomeness, but thought how different it was from his father's fine looks. Seti's hair was jet black, straight, and cut short, not quite to his shoulders. He had a short, black beard cut straight across, and his eyes were black also.

Joe noticed he was wearing a fine white burnous with a wide band of gold thread trimming the edges. He wore a white scarf on his head, held in place by a gold band. Recognizing Seti's formal dress, Joe suddenly realized how important this meeting was to Seti also.

The sun was now low in the sky, but still pushing its heat down on Goshen, so Jacob said, "Let us stay in our family room."

Joe and Pepi sat down on grass mats at the foot of one of the lotus-leaf columns that supported the ceiling. The other children settled on colorful cushions filled with aromatic leaves. Their elders reclined in beautifully carved wooden chairs inlaid with ivory, items which Jacob had managed to keep in spite of the hard times.

"Come in! Come in, my dear Seti," said Joe's father, bowing to his friend.

Chapter 22 – Questions

1. "Anticipate" most nearly means:
   a) look ahead
   b) argue
   c) think
   d) fear

2. What does "succulent" mean? _____
   _____

3-4. What did everyone have for dinner? When could they expect to have it again?

   _____

   _____

5. What did Seti look like? _____

   _____

6. Did Jacob respect Seti? If so, write the line in the story that indicates this.

   _____

   _____

7. What is a "burnous"? _____

   _____

8-9. Did Seti think the meeting was important? Write the line in the story that

   indicates this. _____

   _____

   _____

10. What kind of chairs did Jacob have? _____

   _____

Chapter 23

Jacob waited politely for his friend Seti to speak.

"Jacob, we have known you and your family for a long time, and our families before us have known each other." Jacob nodded, and Seti resumed:

"Even before the terrible plagues came to Egypt, we admired the way you trusted in your God, in your *one* God!

"Then when the plagues came from your God, we realized that only your God had the power of the True God." Seti paused, then continued, "The Egyptian priests always claimed their gods were powerful, but they never proved it!"

Seti paused again, shaking his head. "Now you tell us this powerful God of yours will soon take the firstborn of every Egyptian family."

Joe looked anxiously at Pepi, but Pepi was looking only at his father.

"Jacob, you told us that your God has offered to save also those who would do His Will by putting lamb's blood on their doorways," Seti said.

Again he paused. When he continued, his voice was low but firm, and he enunciated every word very carefully.

"Jacob, my family and I believe in your powerful God and," he drew Pepi close to himself, "we want to do His Will, even as you do."

Seti paused, and the words of Moses suddenly came into Joe's mind again: "Thou shalt fear the Lord thy God, and shalt serve Him only."

Joe's heart was now filled with joy, as Seti continued. "I have talked this over carefully with Tai," he said, looking at his wife holding their baby girl Hatasu, "and we have decided that where you go, we also shall go; and when you leave Egypt, we also shall leave Egypt."

Jacob stood, leaned over his friend, put his arm around his shoulders and said, "We thank the Lord God for your decision, dear Seti."

Ruth then leaned over to Tai and Hatasu, and hugged them, even with Juda still in her arms! Lia jumped up and hugged Hatasu. Joe threw his arms around Pepi and squeezed him as hard as he could.

They were all smiling and half crying at the same time. It was a moment none would ever forget, a moment of joy, a moment of holiness.

Both babies, sensing the feelings of their families, were laughing out loud.

Joe and Pepi sat down, waiting to hear what the fathers would plan for their families. Then Joe remembered that tomorrow would be his birthday.

"What a wonderful birthday present this is," he thought, "to be able to save Pepi and his family from the last terrible plague."

Chapter 23 – Questions

1. What did Seti admire about Jacob?_____
   _____

2. What convinced Seti that Jacob's God was the One True God? _____
   _____

3. What does "enunciated" mean? _____
   _____

4. What did Seti decide to do? _____
   _____

5. Why were the babies laughing? _____
   _____

6-7. Read the words of Our Lord in Luke 15:4-7, and write a sentence
   summarizing the words of Jesus._____
   _____
   _____

8. What were the Israelites to do which showed they were doing God's Will?
   _____
   _____

9. What did Joe think was his best birthday present? _____
   _____

10. What sentence shows that the good example of Joe's family helped Seti's
   family come to their decision?_____
   _____

Chapter 24

It was the third day of the month of Abib. "It's my birthday!" thought Joe as he stirred from his sleep.

On this morning, Joe was awakened by the sound of rain falling softly on the roof, and palm fronds "washing their hands" as Joe's mom called it. He could hear the cries of vendors in the street outside. "Already! I must have slept late!" Then, hearing baby Juda downstairs roaring for his breakfast, Joe *knew* he had overslept, because he usually finished his breakfast before Juda even came downstairs.

His anticipation of what this birthday might bring made him hurry to get dressed. Nevertheless, to please his mother on his birthday, he put on his best white linen tunic. It reached almost to his feet. His mother had made it. She had woven in sky-blue threads as trim around the neckline and the long loose sleeves.

He also took time to say prayers to the Lord God before leaving his room. Then he leaped down the stairs, taking two at a time, and burst into the dining room for breakfast, but instead of just his mother and brother and sister, his father was also there. Then he discovered that Pepi and *his* family were there too! At once they greeted Joe with happy birthday wishes, all smiling and hugging him and urging him to sit down and eat breakfast, which Joe did.

Then, Joe's parents presented him with a beautiful new burnous which had stripes of red, green, yellow, purple, orange, and white. "Just like your patriarch Joseph's coat," declared his mother.

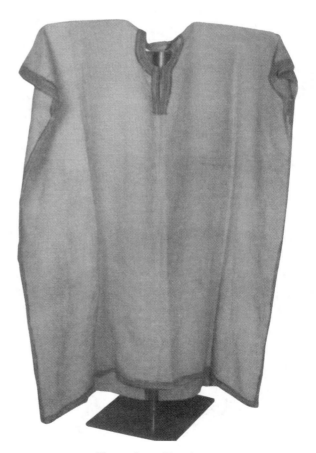

She helped him put on the beautiful garment. Its softness seemed to caress his shoulders, and the colors were a feast for his eyes.

Joe knew exactly how his ancestor, Joseph, felt when he received *his* coat of many colors.

Extra oil lamps were lighted in the room because of the dark rain clouds, but just as Joe put on his coat, the clouds disappeared. Bright sunlight filled the room. With the oil lamps lighted and the brilliant colors of his new coat, Joe's day became very bright indeed!

Egyptian Tunic

"Just like your patriarch Joseph's coat," declared his mother.

Chapter 24 – Questions

1. What is the date of Joe's birthday? _____

   _____

2. How did Joe know he overslept? _____

   _____

3. What is a "vendor"? _____

   _____

4. What did Joe take time to do, even though he was in a hurry? _____

   _____

5-6. What did Joe's parents give him for his birthday? What did it look like?

   _____

   _____

   _____

7. What did the Israelites use to light their rooms?_____

   _____

8. Why do you think Joe was surprised to see his father? _____

   _____

   _____

9-10. The word "bright" is used in two different ways in this chapter. What

   are they? _____

   _____

   _____

Chapter 25

Joe was smiling broadly, but he suddenly wondered why everyone was there at this hour of the morning. Joe said, "I thought—" but his father interrupted. Although he was smiling, his voice was serious. "My dearest firstborn," and he kissed Joe, "your birthday is very important to us all, so we do not want to lessen the celebration, but—" and his face became even more serious, "you recall the words of the Lord God given to us by our great prophet Moses, that on the fourteenth day of this month, we must sacrifice a lamb, and after that, prepare to leave Egypt." He gestured to Pepi and his family. "Our dear friends will join us in the eating of the lamb, which gives us great joy."

Turning back to Joe, his father said, "Because of the great importance of this day in all our lives, but especially because it is your birthday, I am giving you this special amulet, which my father gave me."

As he spoke he took from around his neck a heavy gold chain from which hung a golden "Sign of Life."

"The Pharaoh Ahmosis was so grateful to our patriarch ancestor Joseph for saving Egypt from famine that he gave him this amulet as a sign of gratitude and indebtedness. All your grandfathers have worn it since then."

Joe's throat was suddenly very dry. He could only whisper, "Thank you, Father," and hug his father close.

Joe looked around at his friend Pepi and his family. "I'm surprised to see you all here this morning!" he said.

"Ah, Joe, they are here now to help you celebrate your birthday because we must all start getting ready to do the things that Moses told us the Lord wants," said Joe's father. "We must prepare to leave the land of Egypt."

He looked around at the two families with affection lighting his face. "Let us pray to the Lord," he said.

All knelt as he raised his hands in supplication. "O Lord God, as we celebrate the day on which Thou didst give us our first gift of life, our Joseph, we thank Thee for all the gifts Thou hast given us—our other children as well as our friends. We love Thee and want to do Thy Holy Will in every way and so we beg Thy guidance as we prepare to follow the instructions Thy servant Moses has given us. Long ago, Thou didst give our Fathers this wonderful home in Egypt, and now Thou wilt deliver us from the oppressors and give us a new home where we may serve Thee freely and flourish as a nation."

Jacob then extended his hands over the two families' heads as they continued kneeling. "Lord God, we ask Thy blessing on us and on our nation as we prepare to do Thy Holy Will. We beg Thee to keep us close to Thee and to direct our steps all our lives so that finally we shall be with Thee in Paradise."

Chapter 25 – Questions

1. What is an amulet? _____

   _____

2-4. Where did Jacob get the amulet? What was Joe's reaction to getting the

   amulet? What line in the story demonstrates this?_____

   _____

   _____

   _____

5. Why did Jacob choose Joe's eleventh birthday to give him the amulet?

   _____

6. What did Jacob call Joe as he prayed? _____

   _____

7. What is an *oppressor*? Who were the Israelites' oppressors? _____

   _____

   _____

8. Why did Jacob ask God to "direct our steps"?_____

   _____

   _____

9. What does "flourish" mean? _____

   _____

10. Why did Jacob pray with his family? _____

   _____

   _____

Chapter 26

There was a moment of silence. Baby Juda began to whimper. Jacob lowered his arms. "Juda tells us it is time to begin preparation for our departure out of Egypt," he said.

"But first we shall finish Joe's birthday celebration by enjoying the honey cakes that Ruth prepared for this occasion." At this, Ruth rose, and giving Juda to Joe to hold, she picked up a tray of golden-colored pastries and passed them around to everyone. These cakes were very crisp, being made of unleavened dough, and were Joe's favorite.

As Joe nibbled on his honey cake, his father spoke, "Ruth, thanks for this treat—and I know Joe thanks you, too."

"Yes, thank you, Mother. I really like these cookies," said Joe.

"I liked making them for you, Joe," said Ruth, "and I wish I could make you more but—" and she looked at Jacob questioningly.

"Yes, Ruth, we must begin preparing for our journey," said Jacob, turning to Pepi's father.

"Seti, will you kindly join me in determining just how we can arrange to take goods and flocks with us?"

Seti answered, "I will do whatever you say!"

"Good! Thank you!" said Jacob.

Joe was totally startled by Jacob's next words.

"Moses told us that God has instructed us to ask for gold, silver, and clothing from the Egyptian people who live near us."

Joe was astounded. Lately, the Egyptians had not been very friendly—except for Pepi's family, of course. He thought, "How could they ever give us gold when they won't even say hello to us on the street?" He started to ask his father about it, but it seemed to Joe that Jacob read his thoughts.

Jacob said, "Joe, remember that what the Lord God says cannot be questioned. We cannot know or understand the mind of God, with Whom all things are possible!"

The High Priest blows the "Shofar," signaling a special time or event of the Hebrew nation.

Joe nodded, understanding, at least, his father's words.

Chapter 26 – Questions

1. The families still had over a week to prepare for their trip. Why did they need to start getting ready so soon? _____

    _____

2-3. What did Ruth make Joe for his birthday? Why couldn't Ruth make more?

    _____

    _____

    _____

    _____

4. Why did the Israelites need to ask the Egyptians for gold and silver and clothing?_____

    _____

    _____

5-6. What was Joe's reaction to his father's words? Why? _____

    _____

    _____

    _____

7-9. Did Jacob trust God very much? Write the sentences in this chapter that indicate this. _____

    _____

    _____

    _____

10. What does "astounded" mean? _____

    _____

Chapter 27

By now, Joe was tired of trying to control Juda, who was wiggling and whimpering in his arms, and so he eagerly asked his father, "Please, may I go with you, Father, and help you too?"

"No, dear Joe," Jacob replied, "you will be more helpful by taking care of your brother and sister. Your mother will be very busy preparing a supply of unleavened bread to take on our trip—besides sorting and packing our clothes. You and Pepi must care for the little ones together. That is a big job and must be done."

Joe's stomach was telling him it was almost lunchtime, so he said to Pepi, "If you stay here and watch the kids, I'll get some cheese and fruit, and we can all eat."

Pepi agreed, saying, "I'm hungry, all right!"

Joe set Juda down on a cushion next to a wall and helped Pepi make a kind of fence around the children with chairs and cushions so they could keep the little ones in one place. "Hurry up, Joe! I don't know how long I can keep them together by myself!" exclaimed Pepi.

As Joe prepared the food, he thought, "This is the strangest birthday I ever had! This first month of spring, Abib, we used to go out in the yard and look for new buds of flowers—and Pepi's father took us out to see the new grain in his fields. But now!" Joe felt a shiver up and down his spine. He looked at the gold amulet on the chain around his neck and remembered his father's words about doing God's Will; he knew he had nothing to fear as long as he did God's Will.

Then he recalled his father's other words about the fate of the firstborn of the Egyptians—and he shivered again.

* * * * *

Joe waited patiently in an open field with his father and Pepi and Pepi's father, amidst a large crowd of the men of Israel who lived in Goshen. The men and their sons were assembled as Moses had told them on this evening of the fourteenth day of Abib. Only eleven days before, Joe had celebrated his eleventh birthday; but now he felt much older, as he waited with the leaders of his nation.

The sun was hot, and the field was dusty with so many people trampling the earth. Besides the noise of the crowd, there were bleatings of lambs because each man had a young lamb at his side, as did Jacob. Seti, however, held a large clay basin in his arms. Joe and Pepi held bunches of hyssop in their hands. Sniffing at the pungent sweetness of the leaves, Pepi asked, "Why hyssop?"

"Because it is used to purify things," answered Joe. "Our priests use it in purification ceremonies," he added.

At that moment, Jacob said, "Joe! Here comes our prophet Moses." The crowd raised their voices in greeting as Moses arrived. He stepped up on a large, flat rock and gestured for silence.

He stepped up on a large, flat rock and gestured for silence.

Chapter 27 – Questions

1. Why did Joe want to go with his father? _____

   _____

   _____

2. Why did Jacob tell Joe he could not go with him? _____

   _____

   _____

3. What was Ruth going to pack for the trip? _____

   _____

4. Do you baby-sit for anyone? _____

   _____

5. How had Joe celebrated other birthdays? _____

   _____

6. The weather was warm; why did Joe shiver? _____

   _____

7. On what date did the Israelite men and their sons assemble?_____

   _____

8. Why did they assemble?_____

   _____

9. What is hyssop? _____

   _____

10. How can you tell that the Israelites were preparing for a sacrifice?

    _____

    _____

Chapter 28

As Moses looked over the crowd, his eyes met Joe's for a moment. Joe felt his heart jump a beat as the prophet's eyes seemed to flash into his brain. Then Moses spoke:

"Now is the time for us to fulfill God's Holy Will. Now, all being assembled here together at this hour of evening twilight, it is time to slaughter the lambs. After this, we are to mark our houses with the blood of the lamb which each of us holds."

Moses stopped a moment and closed his eyes. Joe was not sure if it was because the prophet was tired—since he was well over eighty years old—or if he might be praying. Joe had noticed that in spite of his age, Moses had sparkling bright clear blue eyes, not the eyes of an old man but the eager look of a young man. His hair was snowy white and shone in the twilight, "like the evening star," thought Joe. It was thick and wavy, just reaching his shoulders. Moses was tall with an appearance of power, so that no one dared speak until he was finished. All were listening intently as Moses resumed speaking:

"Lord God, we assemble to do Thy Will that we may be saved by the blood of the lamb."

"Now, men of Israel, take some blood from your lamb."

At this, all the men took some blood from their lamb.

Moses spoke again: "Now take your branches of hyssop and dip them in the lamb's blood." When the men had done this, Moses continued. "Now, men of Israel, go home and mark your doorposts and lintels with the blood of the lamb. The Lord will thereby distinguish your homes from those of the Egyptians." Moses stopped again, looking sharply over the crowd to see if all had complied with the commands of the Lord. Seeing that all were ready to leave for their homes, he held out his hand for their attention.

"When you have done this, you must roast some lamb's meat and eat it with unleavened bread and bitter herbs. When you have finished eating, do not save any of it but burn all that is left over." Moses hesitated. "As I told you before, you must be dressed for departure from your homes, even before you eat this meal, so that you will be ready to leave your homes quickly when the time comes.

"The Lord this night will strike down every firstborn, man and beast, in the land of Egypt, except those in the homes marked with the blood of a lamb."

Chapter 28 – Questions

1. What time of day was it when the men assembled? _____
_____

2. Find a sentence that shows how much Moses was respected by his people. _____
_____

3. Why did Joe think Moses might have closed his eyes?_____
_____

4. How old was Moses? _____
_____

5. Moses prayed that the people be "saved by the blood of the lamb." How are we saved in the same way?_____
_____
_____
_____

6. Why did Joe notice Moses' eyes? _____
_____

7. What did Moses say the people were assembled to do? _____
_____

8. Describe Moses' appearance._____
_____

9. What did the Jewish people do with the blood from their lambs? _____
_____
_____

10. What does "complied" mean? Did the Israelites comply with Moses' command?
_____
_____

Chapter 29

Moses stopped speaking and looked at his brother Aaron, standing near him. Aaron nodded at Moses as if in reassurance, and Moses spoke again, louder and stronger than before, each word seeming to carry a great weight.

"The Lord has commanded us to remember forever what we are doing this evening, not only for ourselves but also for our descendants. We shall tell our children, 'This is the Passover sacrifice of the Lord Who passed over the houses of the Israelites in Egypt. When He struck down the Egyptians, He spared our houses.'"

Moses raised his hand above their heads in blessing and said, "Go now to your houses and obey the Lord's commands."

As Joe and his father and friends hurried back to their houses, Joe remembered that his father, and Pepi's father too, had slaughtered lambs and young goats before; but he realized that the slaughter he had just witnessed was very different. His father clumsily held over his shoulder the bag into which he had placed the dead animal. Pepi's father held a cover on the basin, trying to keep the blood from spilling out as they all walked quickly back home.

"Father—" Joe started to ask his father, but Jacob seemed to read his mind, quickly saying, "Yes, Joe, this time the Lord God commanded us to sacrifice, and decreed we would be saved by the blood of a lamb."

Aaron Dressed as the High Priest

Jacob stopped walking and talking for a moment. Pepi and his father stopped also, looking at Jacob. Jacob had a strange expression on his face. He looked up to Heaven for a moment and then at his son and friends.

"The Lord God specifically commanded us to perform this sacrifice so that we may be saved by the blood of this lamb." He took a deep breath and said, "Let us hurry home. We must be ready to be saved by the blood of the lamb of the Lord God."

Chapter 29 – Questions

1. According to the book of Exodus, Moses did not think he was a very good speaker, but his brother Aaron was an excellent speaker. What did Aaron do to reassure Moses?

   _____

   _____

2-3. How important was this night to the Israelites? Write the line in this chapter that indicates this.

   _____

   _____

4-5. Why did the Jewish people take some blood from the lambs?

   _____

   _____

   _____

6. What was Jacob doing when he stopped and looked up to Heaven? _____

   _____

Read Exodus 12:21-28, and answer the following questions.

7. With whom did Moses meet? _____

   _____

8. What angel came to kill the Egyptians?_____

   _____

9. What is the purpose of the Feast of the Passover? _____

   _____

10. When were the Israelites commanded to observe this feast? _____

   _____

Chapter 30

Back home, after packing everything to take to their new home, Joe was very tired, too tired even to try a game of checkers with Pepi. He could see that Pepi was tired too. It was long past their bedtime. They had worked together to bring all the animals of Pepi's family onto the property of Joe's family. Then they dressed for traveling, as Moses had instructed, with their sandals on and their walking staves at hand, even while they ate the roasted lamb meat, the bitter herbs, and the unleavened bread.

Joe felt strange with his sandals on in the house; the family usually left their sandals just outside the door so that the dust from outside would not soil their rugs.

Finally, they all went outside to watch, in the light of a flickering oil lamp held high by Joe's mother, as Jacob dipped the hyssop branches in the basin of lamb's blood which Pepi's father was holding. Jacob sprinkled it all over the doorway on the outside, saying prayers of thanks to the Lord God for His care of them.

Both families consumed almost the entire meal of lamb meat. The two mothers prepared little baskets for the babies to travel in. They also wrapped the unleavened bread, supplies, and clothing they needed for traveling.

By now, it had been dark for some time. All was ready for their trip. The young children were asleep on blankets spread on the family room floor, but the rest were awake, ready to travel. "Where?" thought Joe.

His eyes were getting heavy, so he laid his head down on a cushion on the floor. It was almost midnight when he decided to ask his father where they were going. He saw that all the water had dripped out of the bottom of the cone-shaped clay water-clock, showing that the day was almost finished. Joe went over to his father and smiled.

"Father, I know it is late," he glanced at the water-clock; the water was now totally out of the container. He looked back at his father, "But I—"

Joe never finished his question.

Since Joe's tenth birthday, his father had given him the responsibility of refilling the water-clock, so that now, as he spoke to his father, he automatically reached for the water jug into which the clock-water had dripped; but he stopped suddenly, his hand in midair, as a scream of distress filled everyone's ears. Everyone jerked, staring at one another!

Then all knew that their Egyptian neighbors had been visited by the angel of the Lord God.

Jacob sprinkled the blood of the lamb over the doorway.

Chapter 30 – Questions

1-2. Where did Seti's family move their animals? Why?

_____

_____

3. What did Joe usually do with his sandals? _____

_____

4. Did Joe know where the families were going to go? _____

_____

5-6. What is a water-clock? How does it work?_____

_____

_____

7. Why would the Israelites need staves?_____

_____

8. What did Joe want to ask his father? _____

_____

9. Why were people screaming? _____

_____

10. Were Jacob's family and Seti's family afraid? How can you tell? _____

_____

Egyptian Jewelry

Chapter 31

More screams and cries began to fill the night. Everyone fell to his knees as Jacob prayed:

"Lord God, we Thy people beg Thy forgiveness for ever offending Thee, and we thank Thee for all Thou hast given us.

"We thank Thee now for counting us worthy to be delivered from Thy punishment performed by Thy holy angel. Merciful Lord God, we love Thee ..." Jacob's voice trailed off as more and more screams pierced the silence of the night.

The sounds of soft moaning by the two mothers and the pounding of everyone's hearts could not overcome the shrieks of horror which now seemed to come from every direction.

Joe and his sister Lia were clustered together with their father and mother and baby Juda whom Ruth had snatched out of his basket at the first scream. Next to them, Pepi and his family crouched in fear.

Outer Hall of Ancient Egyptian Temple at Edfu

The screams were still rending the night when a messenger from Moses burst through their door, shouting that it was "time to leave Egypt!" The messenger did not linger as he was running to all the Israelite houses with his message.

Jacob shouted, "Glory to God! Hurry! Everybody gather your things together!"

Around his shoulders, Joe quickly slung a sack packed with his clothing, his checker game, and personal items. He had already loaded one of the ass-drawn carts with his precious stylus and papyrus collection, along with the treasured scrolls. He put his cat on top of his sack so that his pet was peeking over his shoulder, eyes wide with alarm at the humans' commotion.

Suddenly the front door burst open again. This time it was one of their Egyptian neighbors down the street, the father of one of Joe's playmates.

Chapter 31 – Questions

1. What type of prayer did Jacob offer with his family? _____

   _____

2. What is "vengeance"? _____

   _____

3-4. Who burst through the door the first time? Why was he in a hurry? _____

   _____

   _____

Read Exodus 12:29-38 to answer the following questions.

5. Were any Egyptian families spared from the death of their firstborn?

   _____

   _____

6-7. What did Pharaoh tell the Israelites to do? Was he finally repentant?

   _____

   _____

   _____

   _____

8-10. What does the Bible say the people took with them when they left the
      country? What did they take from the Egyptians? How did they do this?

   _____

   _____

   _____

   _____

Chapter 32

Joe was horrified at the sight of the man. The man was in his night clothes, his hair and beard were uncombed, and he had a wild look in his eyes. He had a large sack in his arms, which he thrust at Jacob as he almost screamed in a hoarse voice:

"My son—my Ahmed—is dead!"

Joe shook with fear. He felt his fingers going cold; he had played ball with Ahmed just a few days ago.

Jacob embraced the man, trying to comfort him.

"No—no! You cannot help! But we know that your God did this to us because our Pharaoh would not let you go free."

Tears streamed down his face, and he could not speak. Then, still choking with emotion, the Egyptian father said:

"Jacob, our family wishes you well, but we are afraid your God will kill all the rest of us if you do not go; so to be sure you *do* go—here is silver and gold for your traveling," and he dumped out the large sack on the floor in front of Jacob. Gold coins, gold and silver goblets, and gold jewelry sparkling with precious stones rolled all over the floor.

No one moved, staring at the man, but Jacob stirred himself and grasped the man's hand, saying in a sad voice, "Ahh! Hassam! Our hearts are with you at this terrible time of the Lord God. I wish we could somehow…"

The man interrupted Jacob, crying pitifully, "Enough! Enough! Just go and all your herds with you! We can have no more of you and yours! Ah! I must go back to my family!" and he rushed out the door.

All had been transfixed by the awful sight of the pathetic father. Now, Jacob's voice stirred them into action.

"Come! Come!" His voice was taut with emotion. "Let us all hurry from this dreadful land."

"My son—my Ahmed—is dead!"

Chapter 32 – Questions

1. What horrified Joe? _____

   _____

2. How did Joe react? _____

   _____

3. Whom did the man blame for his son's death? _____

   _____

4. How did Jacob try to comfort the man? _____

   _____

5. What does "transfixed" mean? _____

   _____

6-7. Did Jacob have many fond memories of the land of Egypt? What line in

   this chapter indicates this? _____

   _____

   _____

8-10. The man was upset and sad because God had taken his son. Is there any
   way the man could have avoided this? Did he turn to God once he realized
   the power of God? Why do you think he didn't?

   _____

   _____

   _____

   _____

   _____

Chapter 33

As everyone quickly left the house, they saw many others pouring out of their homes. Some were crying to others about their terrible losses, some shouted to one another to hurry, and others shouted to their animals, urging them on with sticks. It was a bright moonlit night, but many men carried torches, thus causing a jumble of shadows, which, together with the excited voices, made a nightmare scene for Joe.

Joe finished loading the asses and carts, and helped put the little children in a cart with the mothers. Everyone's ears were still filled with the wailing of people in distress which came from everywhere. Joe would have held his hands over his ears, but then he saw his sister Lia holding *her* ears, and he decided he was too old to give in to the noise; so he just hurried along by his mother's side.

The night air was cool, as usual, but Joe felt as if some of the frozen water his father had told him about was sliding down his back. He felt sick to his stomach.

Jacob and Seti gathered the mothers and their children at the edge of town where they had herded their animals—as had all the other Israelite families. There was much dust and confusion, but the bright moonlight showed them their way. The men were pointing to the south, and Joe heard shouts of "Succoth! To Succoth!"

"How far is Succoth, Father?" Joe managed to ask, hurrying with his burden.

"Many miles!" answered his father, "It will take us several days since we'll walk all the way."

Joe was glad he had heeded his mother's order to put on his sturdiest sandals.

Joe rubbed his stomach—but the sight and smell of the lamb's blood on many doorways, people screaming about their dead sons, and the wailing of many at leaving their homes, made a tight knot in Joe's stomach all night.

When Joe and his family, with their friends Seti and his family, left Goshen, the sun was not yet visible in the east as they proceeded south. Joe wondered how far south they might go, remembering what his father had told him about the mountains and glaciers in that direction. All hurried because Pharaoh Mereneptah might change his mind.

Mask of Psusennes I

Chapter 33 – Questions

1. How did Joe feel as he heard the people shouting? _____

_____

2. How did Joe act bravely during this struggle? _____

_____

3. Since it was night, how did all the Israelites find their way? _____

_____

4. What made Joe sick to his stomach? _____

_____

5. To what city were the Israelites going, and which direction was it from Goshen?

_____

_____

6-7. Joe was glad his mother had told him to do something. What was it his mother had told him to do? Why was he glad he had listened to her?

_____

_____

_____

8. Why did everyone hurry? _____

_____

9. How long would it take to reach Succoth, according to Joe's father?

_____

10. How did Joe help in getting ready to start the journey? _____

_____

Chapter 34

Hundreds of Israelites from other settlements joined them on the way as they proceeded toward Succoth. "Why to Succoth, Jacob?" asked Seti.

"Succoth is designated by Moses as the place where the whole nation shall meet to start their journey to Canaan, 'the land of milk and honey' that God promised us for our new home," answered Jacob.

"But Succoth is about 65 miles from here, Jacob," said Seti. "Why don't we travel north and east along the Mediterranean Sea, because that is the shortest route to Canaan?"

"You're right," said Jacob. "That is the shortest way, and we were prepared to go that way. That's why you see our men are armed and our soldiers dressed for battle, because that is also the way to the Philistines, our enemies; but God told Moses we should not go that way because many of our people would be too frightened and run back to Egypt."

Joe spoke up. "*I* would not be afraid of those Philistines!" he boasted as he pulled out his sling.

"And *I* would help too!" declared Pepi; he was always glad to join with Joe in anything!

"Don't worry!" Jacob told them. "All we need fear going this way is that we might get lost in the desert."

By this time, Joe noticed, the morning sun was well up over the horizon. All the people had been moving as fast as they could; so anxious were they to get away from the land of slavery that they had not stopped even to eat. They had not taken time to prepare enough food for the journey. All they had with them was some unleavened bread, which they nibbled as they trudged along.

It was the same unleavened bread that God had directed them to prepare for the night of the Passover of God's avenging angel.

As Joe's mother handed him a piece of the bread, Joe said, "Father told us that God ordered this unleavened bread for us."

"Yes," answered Ruth, "you might call it heavenly bread."

As Joe continued walking determinedly along with the others, he thought of his mother's words: "heavenly bread."

He also recalled his father's words about being saved by the blood of the lamb of God. He could still remember the taste of the lamb he had eaten just last night, and he savored the bread he was eating now.

It suddenly came to him that the Lord God was very close to the Israelites, caring for and protecting them in every way.

"Lord God, I thank Thee," Joe prayed silently.

Hundreds of Israelites from other settlements joined them on the way.

Chapter 34 – Questions

1. Why did the Israelites go to Succoth? _____

    _____

2. How far away was Succoth? _____

    _____

3-4. What was the shortest way to Canaan? Why didn't they go that way?

    _____

    _____

    _____

5. What was the best way to Canaan? _____

    _____

6. How was Joe going to fight the Philistines? _____

    _____

7. How did Joe show his gladness at being away from Egyptian slavery?

    _____

    _____

8. Does Joe pulling out his sling at the thought of the Philistines remind you

    of another Biblical character? Who? _____

    _____

9-10. What was Joe eating on the way? Does this food remind you of another

    similar "food"? _____

    _____

    _____

Chapter 35

It took five days to reach Succoth. The warmth of the late afternoon sun was alleviated by a soft, cooling breeze from the Red Sea when they arrived. Joe and Pepi were fascinated by the huge army of people. "How many are here?" Joe asked his father.

Jacob answered, "I just consulted with our leaders of our town of Goshen. They estimate about 600,000 men, and that's not even counting the women and children! Plus thousands of those friends who are not Israelites whom we are so happy to have with us!" and he gave Seti a friendly pat on the back.

"And that's not counting the animals either!" spoke up Joe. They almost had to shout as they spoke to each other because the noise from the hundreds of herds of sheep and goats, not to mention other animals like Joe's pet cat, was nearly deafening. The only noise heard above the din of the people and animals was the clashing of cymbals and blaring of horns by which several groups of musicians were showing their elation at being free, even though they were bone-tired from the long trip.

The animals were so noisy because they were thirsty and hungry. Many people started to water their beasts and prepare them for camping for the night, but at that moment, messengers came running through the great crowd.

"We are not to camp here!" they shouted. "God has told Moses we must push on to Etham and camp there!"

Pepi's father looked concerned and said to Jacob, "Etham is a three-hour journey east from here. Is it wise to continue on now when we are all so tired and hungry?"

"Seti, we certainly are ready for rest and a meal, but God is wise and knows what is best for us. It is His Will that we move on, and we must always obey His Will, because isn't God's Will immeasurably better than any man's?" Jacob gazed earnestly into the faces of Seti and his family. Joe and his mother and sister Lia had already bowed their heads in acquiescence, and Joe saw that even his baby brother Juda was nodding—but in sleep.

Seti put his arms around his wife Tai and Pepi and their baby girl, Hatasu.

"We have seen the great works of the hands of your God. We want your God to count us as His, and we will obey His Will also."

Mereneptah's coffin lid was never used, because he drowned in the Red Sea.

Chapter 35 – Questions

1. How many people went to Succoth? _____

    _____

2-3. Was it quiet or loud around Joe? Write the line(s) in the story that

    indicate this. _____

    _____

    _____

4. What does "elation" most nearly mean?
    a) anger
    b) great joy
    c) misery

5-6. How much do you think Jacob trusted God? Write the line(s) in this

    chapter that might indicate this. _____

    _____

    _____

7. What great lesson did Seti show he and his family had learned from Jacob?

    _____

    _____

8. What does "acquiescence" most nearly mean?
    a) obedience
    b) amazement
    c) patience

9. "Alleviated" most nearly means:
    a) lessened
    b) increased
    c) modified

Chapter 36

As the huge assemblage prepared to leave Succoth, Seti had another question: "How do we get to this Canaan, the land of milk and honey? Is it far from here?" He looked around, concerned for some of the older men and women and little children riding in carts.

"I know it is far to the east," said Jacob, "but I really don't know the route. In fact, our leaders, just now when I asked them, did not seem to know just how—"

Jacob stopped suddenly, gazing toward the south where Moses and his brother, Aaron, and other leaders were standing at the head of the crowd.

Jacob seemed paralyzed, staring wide-eyed, so that Joe and Pepi and their families all turned to look toward the south also. In fact, all the Israelites began looking and pointing. Cries of awe and prayer were rising from all the people, for, just a few yards in front of Moses and Aaron, an enormous white cloud towering into the blue sky had formed. They saw Moses approach the cloud. Then, turning, he gestured to the people. Quickly, messengers came back through the crowd, saying that God had told Moses they should follow the cloud and in this way, God would lead them to the Promised Land.

"The Lord God be praised!" cried Jacob, and his family said, "Amen."

Joe stared at the cloud and then—without even thinking—he ran through the crowd right past Moses. He stopped a moment near the great prophet, but he just couldn't help it! He ran right up to the cloud; he just had to get a really close look at it, but something stopped him just a few feet from it. Its mistiness seemed to swirl in ever-changing shapes, sometimes slow and then fast. It glowed, with pink, blue, green, and yellow tinting its whiteness. It was an awesome sight, but somehow Joe felt as if it were alive, that he could talk to it!

Then he heard his name called in a commanding tone. "Joseph!" It was Moses' voice.

"Joseph!" said the prophet again. "You are in the presence of great holiness! Do not go any farther!"

By this time, Joe's father had also come up to Moses. He began to apologize for his son, but Moses began to speak.

"Your son has felt the call of the Lord God. Let him stay here near me. My brother Aaron and I will take care of him." So Jacob bowed in assent.

Joe was awestruck, unable to speak, and only nodded his head. "In the presence of great holiness!" Then he knew what had drawn him so powerfully. It was the presence of the Lord God! He felt a surge of emotion that puzzled him, yet which he welcomed. It must be as the great Moses said. "I feel the call of the Lord God," Joe thought. He looked up at the cloud and smiled. Then he turned to look at Moses who smiled at him.

"You are in the presence of great holiness! Do not go any farther!"

Chapter 36 – Questions

1. Why did Moses and Aaron seem lost at first? _____
   _____

2. What was going to help them find their way? _____
   _____

3. Why did Joe run up to the cloud? _____
   _____

4. What did the cloud look like? _____
   _____

5. What did Moses say about the cloud? _____
   _____

6. Why did Moses let Joe stay up near him? _____
   _____

7. We know that today God calls young men to be His priests. Do you think
   they feel as Joe did? _____
   _____

8. How did Joe feel as he realized he had been drawn by the Presence of the
   Lord?
   _____

9. "Jacob bowed in assent." Judging from the story, what does "assent"
   mean?
   _____
   _____

10. What does "awestruck" mean? _____
    _____

Chapter 37

"Come, Joseph, we must hurry to follow the cloud by which the Lord God is guiding us." Joe saw that the cloud was already moving forward along the edge of the desert. He took a place behind Moses and Aaron, following the wonderful cloud. The great nation of Israel followed behind.

Although he had been traveling all day, Joe was so immersed in studying the wonderful cloud that he did not feel tired. He did not even think about feeling tired.

Finally, he heard Aaron say, "How beautiful Etham looks in the evening sun. The white walls of the houses are taking on the peach glow of the sunset."

The cloud, too, was reflecting the evening sun. However, as the sky darkened into night, the cloud seemed to burst into flame. The luminous shapes Joe had seen before now became as tongues of fire! Yet there was no heat, only bright, bright light! Joe marveled at the sight, as did all the Israelites. Cries of praise to God went up from all the people.

The crowd had reached the outskirts of Etham when the fiery column stopped. Moses sent messengers for the Israelites to camp there for the night.

The light was so bright from the blazing column that all were easily able to care for themselves and their flocks.

At last, Joe thought of his family. Excusing himself to Moses, he went back to them. He was still full of the feeling that the cloud had given him. He hoped he could explain it to his father.

Jacob and Seti were settling down with their families for a short meal before sleeping. Joe's father did not reproach Joe for his absence from their midst, because of Moses' words: "Your son has felt the call of the Lord God."

"You do not need to explain, Joseph," said Jacob.

As the sky darkened into night, the cloud seemed to burst into flame.

Chapter 37 – Questions

1. What made Joe forget he was tired? _____

   _____

2. What did the cloud look like at night? _____

   _____

3. How did Moses know God wanted them to stay there for the night?

   _____

   _____

4. What did Joe want to explain to his father? _____

   _____

5. Why didn't Jacob reproach Joe for his absence? _____

   _____

6. What does "immersed" mean? _____

   _____

7. God used a pillar of cloud and fire to direct the Israelites. Today, God usually uses other ways to direct His people. What has Jesus left on Earth to direct the ways of men? Whom do Catholics have today for their leader instead of Moses?

   _____

   _____

   _____

   _____

8. What made all the people begin to praise God? _____

   _____

9. What made the town and the cloud look so beautiful? _____

   _____

10. How could the Israelites see to care for themselves and their animals?

   _____

   _____

Chapter 38

Joe reproached himself for not helping his family during the last march, so he quickly went about watering and feeding their animals, bedding them down for the night and seeing that they were properly tethered. Joe saw that Pepi was busy doing the same thing for *his* family, so he just waved to him. When he finished with the livestock, he hurried to feed and give water to his cat, Dan, which he had heard mewing for quite a while. He saw Pepi feeding his bird Aahmes, a treasured pet because Seti had brought it back to Pepi from a trip to Ethiopia. Joe had just finished with Dan when Pepi came over.

"Why did you stay up there by the cloud?" asked Pepi.

Joe hesitated. "I—don't exactly know," said Joe. "Moses said the cloud was sent by the Lord God to lead us. It—it's a holy cloud—"

"And is this huge column of fire holy, too?" asked Pepi.

"Yes, it is, Pepi," answered Joe. "Moses said the Lord God provided it so that we could travel at night, too. Tonight, we must rest, but Moses said the cloud will lead us to the land of Canaan during the day, and the column of fire will guide us at night. It is a wonderful miracle of the Lord God."

"Just like all those other strange things that happened during the last few months?"

"That's right, Pepi. They were all miracles of the Lord God," said Joe.

Both boys were very tired, but the miracles of the Lord God had captured their minds so that they could think of nothing else.

"My father said that our family would stay with you to find out more about those miracles," said Pepi. "He said we should learn all about your God," he added.

"That's good, Pepi. I can tell you some things about the Lord God, how He has guided our people from the beginning of the world."

"From the beginning of the *world*? When was that?" asked Pepi.

"That was way back when the Lord God talked to Adam and Eve," said Joe.

Just then Pepi's mother called to him to get his supper, so Joe said, "My father can tell you about it tomorrow. He's always teaching me!

"We're sure glad you're with us, Pepi," Joe continued. "When we get to our new home, we will have real peace—no Pharaoh, no slavery, and plenty of time to learn about the Lord God!"

Chapter 38 – Questions

1. How did Joe show his sense of responsibility to his family? _____
   _____

2. How can you tell that Pepi was glad to see Joe? _____
   _____

3. Do you think Pepi believed the "strange things" were miracles?_____
   _____

4. How can you tell that Joe was looking forward to being in the Promised
   Land? _____
   _____

5. Judging from the story, what does "reproached" mean? _____
   _____

6. Judging from the story, what does "tethered" mean? _____
   _____

7-8. What kind of pet did Pepi have? Where did he get it? _____
   _____
   _____

9. Do you think that Joe was looking forward to teaching Pepi about God?
   Have you ever taught a friend about God? We must remember that
   teaching people about God is one of the greatest gifts we can give them.
   _____
   _____
   _____

10. Why did Joe want to stay near the cloud?_____
   _____

Chapter 39

Supper was very brief because everyone was worn out from the long, fast march. The boys helped their fathers set up tents for their families. Before saying good night, Jacob called to Seti to bring his family over so that they could pray together before retiring.

"We realize that you do not know our prayers yet," said Jacob to Seti, "but when we say 'Amen' at the end of each prayer, you can say 'Amen' too.

" 'Amen' means that what we say is true. Do you want to do that?"

"We certainly do, and will. Amen," said Seti, looking around at his family, and they all said "Amen" together.

Next morning, they were awakened early by Moses' messenger.

"Awake! Break up your camp! We must move quickly to Phi-hahiroth! Hurry! Hurry!"

There was great noisy commotion as the Israelites quickly prepared to leave for the new stopping place. Joe asked his father, "Where is Phi-hahiroth?" Joe always liked to know what to expect.

"Directly south of here, two or three hours' march, near where the Red Sea gets very narrow and its waters start to empty into the Mediterranean." He was a little breathless as he struggled with the ropes of their tent.

Just then a pet dog from another family ambled over to investigate Joe's cat seated on top of a bundle of clothes. Dan arched his back and "said" something threatening to the dog. Joe shouted the dog back to his own family, then soothed Dan into settling down again.

Then the Israelite nation started their march to the Red Sea.

Limestone-Raised Relief in the White Chapel at Karnak, Thebes

Chapter 39 – Questions

1. Why did supper go by so quickly? _____

   _____

2. What did the two families do before they went to sleep? _____

   _____

   _____

   Do you do this before you go to sleep? _____

   _____

3. Why did Joe ask his father where they were going? _____

   _____

4. What does "Amen" mean? _____

   _____

5-6. Was Seti acting reverently toward God and respectfully toward Jacob?
   Write the line(s) in this chapter that would indicate this.

   _____

   _____

   _____

7-8. Why did the Israelites have to march to Phi-hahiroth? How far away was it?

   _____

   _____

   _____

9. What does "ambled" mean? _____

10. How is the word "retiring" used in this chapter? _____

   _____

Chapter 40

Jacob moved his family up closer to the front of the crowd; Seti did the same with his family. Jacob wanted Joe to be near Moses and Aaron. He hoped to speak to Moses about Joe. Next year, Joe would be eligible to study for the priesthood, so Jacob wanted Moses' advice. After hearing Moses say Joe had felt "the call of God," Jacob had changed his mind about Joe becoming an artist or scribe.

Joe marched next to Jacob, trying to match his father's strides. Jacob put his arm around Joe's shoulders and said, "You have seen much excitement for a boy of just eleven!"

Joe smiled at his father. Then they both stared at the huge cloud moving forward ahead of them, for the fiery column of the night had changed back to the great cloud that had first appeared the day before. The cloud was so awesome that there was not much talk among the crowd, for they all knew they were in the presence of holiness.

Joe asked, "Will we have to march all day again today, Father?"

"I don't think so," said Jacob, "but I am not sure. Moses' messenger told us that we are to camp at Phi-hahiroth, and that is only about five miles away, on the shore of the Red Sea."

"Maybe we can take a swim!" said Joe. He was getting rather dusty, as were all the people, because they were walking along the edge of the Great Desert.

"We'll see!" said Jacob. He smiled as he thought to himself, "Joe still has boyish desires!"

Pyramids at Giza

92

Chapter 40 – Questions

1-3. Why did Jacob want to be near Moses? What did Jacob think Joe should

be when he grew up? What made him think that?_____

_____

_____

_____

4-5. Why was there not much talking in the crowd? Is it proper to talk under
these circumstances? Is it proper to talk loudly after Mass?

_____

_____

_____

6. What other professions had Jacob previously hoped Joe might follow?

_____

_____

7. Where was Phi-hahiroth located? _____

_____

8. What did Joe want to do when he got there? Why? _____

_____

9. Why were the conditions on the march so dusty? _____

_____

10. Why did Jacob smile at Joe's hope to go swimming?_____

_____

Chapter 41

The morning sun was still not very high above the horizon when the Israelites arrived at Phi-hahiroth, a small fishing village of tents and a few brick huts. This was a settlement of only Egyptians, and there were signs of mourning and preparations for funerals all through the village. The beautiful holy cloud led the Israelite nation past the settlement. They saw many people turn their faces away from them as they recognized the Israelites.

As they marched, Joe saw some fishermen's boats on the beach. He saw the fishermen's nets spread out to dry. Here and there, Joe saw a dead sheep or an ox, abandoned by their owners. No one was working; all were grieving for their dead firstborn. Joe saw his father looking at the mourners in sorrow.

As Seti walked along, he put his arms around Pepi, holding him close and saying, "The God of the Israelites has spared us," to which Pepi's mother responded, "Amen."

"Did we ever have any fish to eat, Father?" said Joe, trying to lift Jacob from his sadness.

"We did a long time ago when you were a baby," answered Jacob. His face was somber as he recalled that he had not been able to go fishing since Pharaoh had forced him and his fellow Israelites into the slavery of making bricks for their great pyramid-tombs. Jacob saw that Joe was looking at him anxiously, so he quickly smiled and said, "But when we reach Canaan, we will fish!"

Man Hunting Birds in Marshes with Wife and Daughter

Just then they both saw that the holy cloud had stopped. They had passed the village and reached the shore of the sea. Pepi's father came up to them and said, "Does the cloud stopping mean we are to camp here?"

Jacob answered, "It must be, but I wonder—" Then the word came from Moses that they were to camp by the shore. Everyone was puzzled, because they assumed that they would continue marching beside the sea until the end of the day. However, the holy cloud had definitely stopped, remaining in front of them.

The men pitched their tents, and the women tended to the children and prepared for a meal. The men gathered in little groups and tried to understand why their march was stopped by the seashore.

Chapter 41 – Questions

1. What time did the Israelites arrive at Phi-hahiroth? _____

_____

2. What was the occupation of the villagers? _____

_____

3. Why hadn't Jacob been fishing for a long time? _____

_____

4. What did Jacob want to do when he reached Canaan? _____

_____

5. Why did everyone think they would not stop at Phi-hahiroth? _____

_____

_____

6-7. Jacob felt compassion for the mourners in the village. How did Joe try to relieve him of his sadness? How would you have felt if you were Jacob?

_____

_____

_____

8. The men gathered in groups to discuss why they were stopped in front of the Red Sea. Do you think they were having doubts? Considering all of God's miracles in the past few days, should they have had any doubts?

_____

_____

_____

9. How can you tell that the villagers of Phi-hahiroth also had felt God's punishment? _____

_____

10. How did the Israelite men feel about stopping by the seashore? Why?

_____

_____

_____

Chapter 42

"Surely, we're not going to cross the sea!" said one man, laughing as he gestured to the water. "There are not enough boats here—and we can't *swim* across!"

On the other side of the sea, on the east shore of the Red Sea, they could just barely see another settlement. "That's Baal-Saphon," said Jacob. Then he looked along the shoreline where they stood. "Even as narrow as it is here," he nodded, "you're right. We could not cross it!"

The men shook their heads in bewilderment, but Jacob said, "Never fear. The Lord God is protecting us and will guide us."

They were still gazing out over the sea when loud shouts began coming from the other end of the huge throng, from those who were at the rear.

Joe was helping his mother when he heard the tumult. Running up to his father, he cried, "Father! What is it?" for Joe was not tall enough to see over the crowd.

Jacob and the men around him—and now the women too—were straining their eyes to see—what?

"Father! Father! What do you see?" cried Joe.

"It—it is Pharaoh's army!" exclaimed Jacob. His words were echoed all through the crowd—"Pharaoh's army! Pharaoh's army!"

Just where the sky met the sand, they could see a great cloud of dust—and then a dark line in front moving rapidly toward them. Flashes of sunlight glinted on spears and armor. As the line came nearer—though still about a mile away—they could discern Pharaoh's soldiers and chariots drawn by galloping horses.

Screams of fright began to rise from the crowd. Some began to shout in great agitation, "Moses! Moses! Are we to die here in the desert? Lord God, save us from Pharaoh!"

Some men even reproached Moses, shouting, "We would be better off still serving the Egyptians than dying here in this desolate place!" Many men were praying with their families, as were Jacob and Seti.

King Tut's Golden Throne

"It — it is Pharaoh's army!" exclaimed Jacob.

Chapter 42 – Questions

1. Why did they think they could not cross the Red Sea?_____

_____

2. How did Jacob show his faith in God? _____

_____

3. What does "bewilderment" mean? _____

_____

4. What does "tumult" mean? _____

_____

5. What were the Israelites shouting about?_____

_____

6. Why do you think that sometimes God gives us burdens?_____

_____

7. Do you think that some of the Israelites forgot that God was taking care of
   them? Why or why not? _____

_____

_____

8. What was the most important reason why God protected the Israelites?
   (Choose the best answer.)

   a) They suffered enough as slaves.

   b) God does not want anybody to be hurt.

   c) It was from that nation that the Savior of the world was to come.

9. What does "agitation" mean? _____

_____

10. What does "desolate" mean? _____

_____

Chapter 43

Then they saw Moses pointing to the holy cloud. It was moving rapidly—not forward as before, but around them to the rear of the crowd. Then it stopped, so that it was between them and the Egyptians. Thus, they could not see the Egyptians—and the Egyptians could not see them!

Over the crowd's screaming, Joe heard his father shout, "Stop! Listen! Be quiet—the Egyptians have stopped! Listen! We can't hear the thunder of the horses' hooves any more!"

The crowd quieted down.

It was true.

Whereas before all had heard the great noise of the approaching army, now they heard nothing!

Moses ordered everyone to stay camped where they were, because some had already pulled up stakes to run away. Joe felt very confused about whether to go or stay, but he really wanted to stay with the protection of the wonderful cloud provided by the Lord God.

Gradually the crowd calmed down, seeing that the cloud was hiding them from Pharaoh's army. Joe and his family tried to make themselves comfortable without setting up too much of their camp. No one put up his tent. Some argued with one another and some with Aaron, but most surrounded Moses, seeking his advice. Joe saw Jacob talking with Aaron, and he wondered what Aaron said.

The holy cloud remained between the Israelites and Pharaoh's army all day. Joe and Pepi, having finished helping their families with various chores, decided to take a swim in the Red Sea. They waded into the water and found that the sandy bottom began to incline quite soon from the shore, so they stayed close to the shore. Quite a few of the boys and some men had decided to take a swim also, but the mothers and children merely watched the splashing and leaping.

The boys spent most of the afternoon in the water. It felt so good after their hot, dusty march of the day before.

By late afternoon, Joe asked Pepi, "Are you hungry?" Of course, Pepi answered, "I sure am!"

Joe said, "Maybe we can find some clams or something in the wet sand."

"I have a little shovel in my pack—shall I go get it?" asked Pepi.

"That's a good idea. I'll get mine too!"

Returning in a few minutes, the boys started digging in the sand, and sure enough, they turned up a whole bed of clams and lots of little wrigglers! When the other men and boys saw this, they all started digging too—and the food of the sea gave all the people the refreshment they needed.

The food of the sea gave all the people the refreshment they needed.

Chapter 43 – Questions

1-2. What happened to the cloud? What effect did it have?_____

_____

_____

3. How long did the holy cloud stay between the Egyptians and the Israelites?

_____

4-5. What did Joe and Pepi do during this time? What did they notice about the Red Sea's depth? _____

_____

_____

6-7. What did the boys eat for lunch? How did they get them? _____

_____

_____

8. Considering that God sent the ten plagues to Egypt, and even had an angel of death kill Pharaoh's firstborn son, do you think Pharaoh was being stubborn? Why do you think he would chase the Israelites after seeing the power of God firsthand?

_____

_____

_____

9. Before Moses ordered them to stay where they were, what had some of the Israelites done? _____

_____

10. What do you think the Egyptians were doing on the other side of the holy cloud?_____

_____

Chapter 44

"Father, look how the holy cloud is spread so wide!" said Joe as the two families sat together after supping.

"Yes," said Jacob, "the sun is going down and the Lord is providing us protection from Pharaoh! I also heard Aaron say the cloud is black on the Egyptian side."

They sat admiring the Lord God's work for a few minutes and then a message came from Moses:

"Prepare to march! Prepare to march!"

Jacob grabbed the messenger by his arm. "Where to?" he demanded; but the messenger shook him off, saying, "I do not know!" He added, "Our spies tell us that the Egyptians are more confused than we are! That's all I know!" and he ran with his message to the other Israelites.

All the people were bustling about, wondering what would happen next. Jacob and Seti checked preparations with their families. Joe made sure his cat had a safe traveling spot. Pepi came over to Joe and said, "It's kind of scary, isn't it?"

Joe answered, "We know that the Lord God is guiding us, so we don't need to be scared, but I can't help being a little afraid, too, Pepi."

So, the Egyptians and the Israelites could not see each other as the Israelites waited on the shore of the Red Sea, because the holy cloud formed a huge wall: dark on the Egyptian side, but bright on the Israelite side. The Israelites could see the serene sea beside them, now brightly lit by the moon's silvery beams shining on its surface. "That's a beautiful sight," said Ruth to Jacob.

The Israelites tried to sleep a little that night, despite the fact that they were still packed and ready to march whenever the command came. It was quiet, but an uneasy quiet.

All through the night, the moon lit up the calm surface of the Red Sea. Joe finally slept and dreamed he was playing checkers with his cat. It did not seem a bit unusual!

Joe was awakened by Dan calling for his breakfast. Joe fed him a tidbit from the night before. Then he thought about the enemy on the other side of the cloud.

Despite the fact that he knew he should trust in the Lord God, Joe was afraid of the Egyptians like everyone else. He decided to ask, "Father, can't we go to Moses and ask him what we can do to escape?"

Jacob nodded, and taking Joe by the hand, quickly walked to where Moses stood by the water's edge with Aaron and the other leaders.

Moses' eyes were closed, apparently in prayer, and his staff was clasped tightly in both hands in front of him. The men stared at him intently, saying nothing. Other Israelites came up to Moses at the same time, anxiously asking what was to become of them.

Chapter 44 – Questions

1. What changed about the cloud? _____
_____

2-3. What was the message of Moses? What did Jacob ask the messenger?
_____
_____

4. Were Joe and Pepi scared? _____
_____

5. What did Joe dream about?_____
_____

6-7. What did Joe ask his father? What did his father do?_____
_____
_____

8. What was Moses doing? _____

9. Judging from the story, what do you think "serene" means?
    a) very calm and clear
    b) scary
    c) violent

10. What does "intently" mean? _____

Chapter 45

Then Joe saw Moses open his eyes and turn to look at those around him. He looked at Joe for more than a moment and then loudly made an announcement.

"Fear not! Stand your ground, and you will see the victory the Lord will win for you today!"

"Today! Today! Today!" echoed through the crowd.

He paused and then pointed to where the Pharaoh's army was hidden behind the holy cloud.

"These Egyptians whom you see today you will never see again." His voice became louder.

"The Lord Himself will fight for you; you have only to keep still."

Some of the men shook their heads, grumbling at these words, but then Jacob declared to all, "We must show our trust in the Lord God by showing our trust in His servant Moses!"

The grumblers became silent, but all were puzzled.

Then, as they watched him, Moses turned back, facing the sea. He strode to the very edge of the water so that the tips of his sandals became wet.

Slowly, he raised his right hand over the sea, still firmly clasping his staff. Then he raised his left hand high.

His arms were extended over the Red Sea for just a moment, when everyone heard a loud wind.

"There must be a storm coming," thought Joe. All heard the sound of the wind become a roar. It was blowing from the east toward themselves.

The sun in the clear morning sky lit up the whole expanse of the Red Sea.

The wind blew stronger. Joe could feel the air stirring about his shoulders and blowing hot against his face, but he saw no clouds.

Moses continued to hold his hands high over the sea. The Israelites were murmuring in bewilderment, and Joe cried, "What is happening, Father?" Jacob just shook his head, watching Moses.

Stained-Glass Window of Moses

Chapter 45 – Questions

1. Did Moses know that God would save them? _____

_____

2. Did all the people believe Moses when he said God would protect them?

What indicates this in the story? _____

_____

_____

3. What did Moses tell the men to do? _____

_____

4. What did Jacob say to support Moses? _____

_____

5-6. What time of day was it that Moses lifted his staff toward the Red Sea?

What line of the story indicates this? _____

_____

_____

7. Did Joe think a storm was coming?_____

_____

8. What does "strode" mean? _____

_____

9. What does "murmuring" mean? _____

_____

10. What is "bewilderment"? _____

_____

Chapter 46

The wind blew hotter and much harder until it sounded like—like—but Joe could compare it to nothing in his experience. It was much louder than even the galloping Egyptian horses had sounded earlier.

"There is not even any thunder!" said Joe. "It reminds me of the crowd roaring at Pharaoh's celebration!" said Jacob.

The crowd of Israelites was not roaring, however. The people gathered at the edge of the water, their robes and hair blowing straight back in the wind. They stared in fascination at the water as the hot wind blew across it from the opposite shore, from the east. They wiped perspiration from their faces. The mothers covered their babies' faces to protect them from the hot wind.

Joe could not move as he stared at the sea. The great wind was forming a huge sort of dent in the water. The dent rapidly became deeper, reaching all the way across to the far shore.

Then Joe saw waves forming on both sides of the "dent"—but they were going in opposite directions—to the right and to the left—at the same time!

Moses continued to hold his hands high over the sea.

Joe echoed the crowd: "What is happening, Father?" Jacob just shook his head.

The wind continued blowing, growing louder than anything Joe had ever heard. No one could shout loudly enough to be heard over it.

Now Joe saw the "dent" in the sea becoming deeper, "like when I plowed a furrow for my garden!"

To the right and to the left, the sea was greatly agitated, the waves getting bigger and bigger and flowing away from the "dent" in front of the people. All watched the phenomenon, fascinated at the sight of the sea dividing.

"The opening must be as wide as the plaza of the temple back in Egypt!" exclaimed Joe's father.

Scroll and "Tad" or Pointer

106

The dent rapidly became deeper, reaching all the way across to the far shore.

Chapter 46 – Questions

1. What was the wind like? Which way was it blowing? _____

   _____

2. How loud was it? _____

   _____

3. What happened to the Red Sea? _____

   _____

4. When Joe asked him, did Jacob know what Moses was doing? _____

   _____

5-6. Why could Joe not move? What in the story indicates this? _____

   _____

   _____

7. From the story, what does "agitated" mean? _____

   _____

8. What is a "phenomenon"? _____

   _____

9. What is a "furrow"? _____

   _____

10. Do you think the Israelites felt safer after seeing the power of God

   once again? _____

   _____

   _____

Chapter 47

Joe now saw huge waves leaping around on both sides of the "dent."

The "dent" was now wider and deeper, more like a trough. Joe saw that the water that had been near their feet was now moving away from them, sideways, to their right and to their left. The sea was actually dividing into two parts!

"Father!" shouted Joe, but the hot wind blew into his mouth and blew away any more words.

With a fierce strength, the hot wind kept pushing the water more and more to the right and to the left, so that the water at the bottom of the trough was now far lower than the water on the right and on the left.

"It's like walls of water!" exclaimed Joe to himself, "and they're getting farther and farther apart!"

The men were shouting now. All saw the division in the water becoming wider at their feet. They could see the floor of the sea as it sloped down to the center of the sea.

"Father!" shouted Joe. "Where is the water going?"

Jacob pointed to his left. He shouted, "It normally empties into the Mediterranean, but"—then he pointed to his right—"but now it is also being pushed back into the main body of the sea where it is very large, much larger than here!"

All through the day, God made the wind blow on the Red Sea. All forgot their fatigue as they watched the dividing of the sea. What did it mean? Why was it happening?

As the walls of water spread farther apart, Joe could see more and more of the sea floor. Joe saw sea plants wilted and flattened by the hot wind. He could see crabs scrambling towards the watery walls, which were rapidly moving away from them.

"If this keeps up," thought Joe, "we'll soon see the bottom all the way to the other side!" Joe heard his father shout to Seti that the opening was now over a 100 cubits wide and it was still getting wider. And the surface of the sea stayed at its original level.

Everyone still felt the hot wind blowing against them, but the main force of the wind was on the sea itself. "Otherwise, we would be blown off our feet!" shouted Seti.

Even after sunset, everyone still watched the sea in the bright moonlight, and the light of the holy cloud.

No one could sleep, except the babies. All were astounded at the ever-widening break in the sea. The night was filled with the thundering of the waves crashing against each other combined with the deafening roar of the great wind forcing apart the walls of water.

Chapter 47 – Questions

1. What is a "trough"? _____
   _____

2. What did Joe say the formation of water looked like? _____
   _____

3-4. Could anyone sleep? Could you sleep through this incredible miracle?
   _____
   _____
   _____

5. Why did everyone forget their fatigue? _____
   _____

6. Have you ever been so excited or anxious that you forgot how tired or
   sleepy you were? When?_____
   _____

7. How wide was the opening? _____
   _____

8. Did Joe know why the water was forming in this way? What line of the
   story would indicate this? _____
   _____

9. How could the people see what was happening after sunset?_____
   _____

10. What words are used in the story to explain how loud the wind and
    water were?_____
    _____

Chapter 48

Now Joe saw that where the water had been, the seabed was drying up! Where the water had been lapping at his feet, the sand was now totally dry. He saw the steep incline of the seabed in front of him, where just a few hours before he and Pepi had been splashing around. He saw that the sea floor dipped sharply down to the middle of the seabed. The hot wind was totally drying up the floor of the sea. Water plants were shriveling up and drying in the wind.

Finally, the wind stopped as suddenly as it had started. A great, wide stretch of space separated the walls of water whose surface was still agitated by turbulent waves.

"That's almost 300 feet wide!" exclaimed Jacob. All the Israelites were exclaiming over the phenomenon, some in amazement and some in fear.

It was near midnight. Moses had lowered his hands as soon as the water had started to part, but stayed at the front of the multitude watching the miracle with the others, leaning on his staff.

Now, when the wind died down, he turned to face his people. He raised a loud voice to quiet the crowd.

"The Lord God has shown us the way! Let us go!" and he pointed out over the opening in the sea.

Almost with one voice, the people gave a loud shout of praise to the Lord for showing them His way to deliverance from evil.

"The Lord God has shown us the way! Let us go!"

Chapter 48 – Questions

1. How dry was the sand?_____

_____

2. What does "turbulent" mean?_____

_____

3. What did Joe notice about the seabed? _____

_____

4. Why were some Israelites fearful?_____

_____

_____

5. How wide was the opening when the wind died down? _____

_____

6. Why do you think God made the opening so wide? _____

_____

7. Why were some of the Israelites still afraid? _____

_____

_____

8. Did all of the Israelites finally realize that God would save them?_____

_____

_____

9. What time of day was it when Moses told the people it was time to go?

_____

_____

10. Did the Israelites take time to thank God for their deliverance?_____

_____

Chapter 49

The great wind had stopped, but all heard the turbulence of the waves plunging against each other on each side of the huge opening.

Everyone quickly gathered up their belongings. It was still the darkness of night.

Moses strode firmly forward and down the sandy slope of the seabed, his silvery hair and beard shining like a beacon in the brightness of the holy cloud.

Aaron gestured widely to the people, pointing to the far shore.

Then the great throng of people surged forward. It was just after midnight. They had to walk only three-quarters of a mile to the other shore, but it was not an easy trip! They had to walk down the first steep slope of the seabed and then struggle up the other side's steep slope to the shoreline. With their flocks, property, carts, and people who could not walk, it took them about three hours to walk to the other side, shortly before dawn, about 3 a.m. God had made the sandy seabed smooth and solid for them to walk over it.

They drove their animals down onto the dry bed of the sea. They stared nervously at the rippling walls of water, at the same time marveling at the works of the Lord God. The waves of the sea high above their heads clashed like cymbals as they hurled themselves together, loudly objecting to their strange displacement.

Jacob and Seti kept their families near the watery walls, fearing the press of anxious people in the middle of the great throng. The two fathers kept themselves between their families and the hastening people, the mothers and small children walking between the fathers and the big boys. Thus, Joe and Pepi found themselves moving fast next to the wall of water on the right side.

Joe and Pepi, like many of the children, found it irresistible to stick their hands into the water of the walls! Joe put his hand into the water up to his elbow, splashing himself all over as he moved along—and so did Pepi. The wall kept its vertical position. The boys showed their fathers their wet hands.

Jacob said, "The Lord God is mighty— His strength is past our comprehension!"

"Amen!" said Seti.

Sea Battle

114

Chapter 49 – Questions

1. Who was the first to cross the dry seabed? _____

   _____

2. What is a beacon? _____

   _____

3. Were the people still afraid? Why or why not? _____

   _____

   _____

4. Why did Joe's and Pepi's families both stay near the wall? _____

   _____

   _____

5. What did the waves sound like? _____

   _____

6. What does it mean when the story says that the waves were "objecting to
   their strange displacement"? _____

   _____

7-8. What did Pepi and Joe find irresistible? What happened? _____

   _____

   _____

9. What was Jacob's reaction? _____

   _____

10. What word did Seti use that he had just learned, that showed he believed
    that the God of the Israelites was the True God? _____

Chapter 50

The boys were very excited. "Look, Father!" cried Joe. "We can see big fish swimming around in there!" He put his hand deep into the water, trying to catch one, but it wiggled away.

The holy cloud was shining brightly behind them, making day out of night. The boys could easily see the silvery fish slithering around inside the water.

"Joe," cried Pepi, "look down there—see! Ferns growing!" Joe looked at the ferns waving with the movement of the water. He put his hand in the water and pulled out a piece of the fern. He showed his father the dripping plant.

Jacob nodded. "Yes, it's wonderful!" he said. "But we must hurry and get to the other shore before the Egyptians find out we have left!"

Seashells were scattered all over the seabed, and Joe and Pepi snatched up many of them for proof of the fantastic miracle. Everyone was exclaiming as they hastened along. All marveled at the walls of water high above their heads. The sand of the sea where they walked was absolutely dry like the desert. Some ventured to pull out a handful of wet sand from the other side of the wall. They planned to keep the sand, shells, and ferns in remembrance of the time God saved them.

When Moses reached the far shore of the sea, Joe saw him turn and face the Israelites still coming across, watching them carefully. Jacob explained to Joe, "He wants them to see him standing there in order to give encouragement to any who might become faint-hearted."

As the last man with all his flocks before him set foot on the eastern shore and stood before Moses, a cheer went up from the Israelites. They thanked God for their miraculous escape from the Egyptians. Then the holy cloud moved from the water to the sea shoreline near them.

Suddenly, by the light of the cloud, they saw a dark line forming on the far shore they had just left.

It was the Egyptians!

Joe gasped. Shouts of gladness turned into shrieks of fear, as Pharaoh, his chariots, and his soldiers quickly started down the slope of the seabed on the other side—coming along the same dry seabed the Israelites had just traversed!

"Father! Father! They're going to catch us!" cried Joe, tugging at Jacob's arm. "Let's run!"

Jacob restrained him by saying, "Joe! Stop! Trust in the Lord God."

He put his hand in the water, trying to catch a fish.

Chapter 50 – Questions

1-2. What happened to the fish during this time? Was God protecting all

His creatures? _____

_____

_____

3. Why was it so bright outside? _____

_____

4. What things did the Israelites pick up from the seabed? _____

_____

5. Why did they want to keep them? _____

_____

_____

6. Why did Moses turn and face the people who were still coming across?

_____

_____

7. Whom did the Israelites see on the far side of the water from which

they had just come? _____

_____

_____

8-10. Were the Israelites frightened? Did they still lack faith? Did Jacob?

_____

_____

_____

Chapter 51

Joe could plainly see the Egyptians—and hear them, too—as they shouted and whipped their horses, urging them toward the Israelites.

Then Joe heard a tremendous peal of thunder come from the holy cloud. It was so loud and sudden that everybody jumped. Instantly, from the cloud, a huge bolt of lightning shot down on Pharaoh Mereneptah and the men near him. They were killed and fell into the dry seabed.

Now Joe saw the charioteers and horses and foot-soldiers staggering in confusion. He heard their shouts: "Let's get out of here!" "Go back! Go back!" and "The God of the Israelites is fighting us!" Joe heard Pharaoh's officers ordering the soldiers to get the chariots running again, but the confusion was too great. They kept pushing into one another's chariots and became even more bogged down in the wet sand. Joe could hear the Egyptians' trumpets sounding retreat, but no one could move anywhere.

"Father!" shouted Joe. He had to shout over the crowd's roar as they saw the Egyptians drowned. "Father! They are trying to turn around! They're trying to go back!" Jacob could only nod, for he was shouting along with his family, along with Seti and his family, and along with all the Israelites. Even the animals were bleating and baying at the thunderous noise from the holy cloud and the tumultuous roar of the soldiers.

"Father! Father! Look at Moses!" shouted Joe.

Moses still stood at the shore's edge where all could see him.

He suddenly raised his hands and stretched them high over the dry seabed. Pharaoh's army was still struggling to turn around their chariots! The foot soldiers were running back and forth, trying to climb over one another, struggling to get back to the shore.

Suddenly, Joe heard their shouts turn into screams of terror. The huge walls of water suddenly came rushing down from both sides on the Egyptian soldiers and their

horses and chariots. With a deep rumbling roar, the walls of water hurled themselves at each other as if venting their anger at their separation. The moon was losing its light as the morning sun rose, lighting up the churning waters, which now were burying the Egyptian soldiers.

The churning waters buried the Egyptian soldiers and their chariots.

Chapter 51 – Questions

1-2. How did the Pharaoh die? How did his officers react to his death? _____

_____

_____

3. Why couldn't they get back to the entrance of the sea? _____

_____

4. What does "tumultuous" mean? _____

_____

5-6. What did Moses do with his hands? What happened next? _____

_____

_____

Read Exodus 14:26-31 and answer the following questions.

7-8. Were all the Egyptians killed? Write the passage in the Bible that

indicates this. _____

_____

_____

9-10. Did the Israelites gain more faith in God after seeing all this
happening? _____

Do you think that God sometimes gives us hardships so that our trust will
be increased? Has there been a time in your life when you know that God

helped you in some special way? _____

_____

_____

_____

_____

Chapter 52

The Egyptians disappeared from Joe's sight, but they suddenly reappeared. They were tossed high in the air on towering geysers of white foam shooting up into the sky as the walls of water met. The wildly churning water tossed them around like leaves in a sandstorm, thought Joe.

At the shoreline where the Israelites stood with Moses, water was forced up to their feet, so they moved back a little. After about ten minutes, the horrendous churning of the water finally calmed down.

In silent awe, the Israelites watched this latest evidence of the Lord God's might. There was no one to be seen in the water anymore. Joe remembered Moses' words: "These Egyptians whom you see today, you will never see again!"

Gradually, Joe and his family and all the others aroused themselves from the terrible catastrophe they had just witnessed. Prayers of thanksgiving went up from the crowd, praising the glory of the Lord God.

Seti said to Jacob, "Is that glow on our faces more from the dawn's sun or from the happiness of deliverance?"

"They are both from God," answered Jacob, and he smiled.

Seti said, "Amen."

Joe was glowing inside as he realized Pepi would soon be learning truths revealed by the One True God.

Passage of the Jews through the Red Sea (Ivan Aivazovsky)

122

Chapter 52 – Questions

1. What is a "geyser"? Have you ever seen one? _____
   _____

2. Why did the Israelites need to move back? _____
   _____

3. Of what did the Egyptians in the churning water remind Joe? _____
   _____

4. How high did the geysers shoot? _____
   _____

5. What prophecy of Moses came true? _____
   _____

6. What kind of prayers did the Israelites offer? _____
   _____

7. Why was Joe happy for Pepi? _____
   _____

8. Do you think Pepi believed in the One True God now? _____
   _____

9. Pharaoh's men paid with their lives for listening to the evil Pharaoh and
   refusing to obey God. Do you think the Israelites felt any sorrow for
   these Egyptians? _____
   _____
   _____

10. What is meant by the phrase "Joe was glowing inside"? _____
    _____

Chapter 53

Moses gathered the people around him to praise the Lord in song. He started by singing.

"I will sing to the Lord for He is gloriously triumphant; horse and chariot He has cast into the sea. My strength and my courage is the Lord, and He has been my Savior. He is my God. I praise Him, the God of my father; I extol Him."

Moses sang many more verses in praise of God Almighty, but Joe could not remember them all.

"Our scribes will write it all down, and you can study them later during lessons with your mother," Jacob told him. Then and there, Joe decided to be a scribe like his father.

Joe and his family, with Pepi and Pepi's family, watched Aaron's sister Miriam take a tambourine in her hand to sing and dance in praise of the Lord God.

"She's a prophetess," Joe whispered to Pepi as they watched her twirling and dipping to her music.

On seeing her dancing, many of the other women—including both Joe's and Pepi's mothers—took up their tambourines and followed Miriam's lead, singing and dancing in praise of the Lord God.

The Crossing of the Red Sea (Nicolas Poussin)

Miriam took a tambourine in her hand and began to sing and dance in praise of the Lord.

Chapter 53 – Questions

1. How did Moses praise the Lord? _____

   _____

2. What does "extol" mean? _____

   _____

3. Who was going to record the crossing of the Red Sea? _____

   _____

4. What did Joe decide he wanted to be when he grew up? _____

   _____

5-6. Who was Miriam? What is a tambourine? _____

   _____

7. Who danced along with Miriam? _____

   _____

Read Exodus 15:1-18 and answer the following questions.

8-10. Moses uses many similes (a phrase using "like" or "as" to make a
comparison) in his song. Point out at least three of them.

   _____

   _____

   _____

   _____

Chapter 54

The Israelites spent the whole day alternately singing and resting, praising God all the time. Moses sang many verses to God's glory.

After each one, Miriam and the other Israelite women sang this verse:

"Sing to the Lord for He is gloriously triumphant;
Horse and chariot He has thrown into the sea."

Joe sat next to his father while watching the dancing. Joe kept his arm around Lia, and his father held Juda, who was clapping his hands to the music.

Pepi and Seti sat next to them with their baby Hatasu.

"I will never forget this time, Father," said Joe. Joe saw his father's eye glistening with a tear. Joe leaned toward his father anxiously and put his arm around him.

Then Joe's father said, "Though you are only eleven years old, my dear son — today you are a man!"

Not the End:
A New Beginning for the Israelites!

Moses Strikes the Rock (Raphael)

Chapter 54 – Questions

1. What did the Israelites do all day? _____

   _____

2. When did Miriam and the other women sing the verse quoted? _____

   _____

3. What did Joe do during this time? _____

   _____

4. What was the baby Juda doing during this dancing? _____

   _____

5. Why did Joe's father cry? _____

   _____

6. What did Jacob mean when he said that, today, Joe was a man? _____

   _____

   _____

7. What things had Joe learned during these events? _____

   _____

8-10. Can you see how God protected His people throughout these events?

   Point out at least three examples. _____

   _____

   _____

   _____

   _____

   _____

NOTES

NOTES

NOTES

NOTES

NOTES

NOTES